Challenges to Fingerprints

Lyn Haber, Ph.D.
Ralph Norman Haber, Ph.D.

Lawyers & Judges Publishing Company, Inc.
Tucson, Arizona

This publication is designed to provide accurate and authoritative information in regard to the subject matter covered. It is sold with the understanding that the publisher is not engaged in rendering legal, accounting, or other professional service. If legal advice or other expert assistance is required, the services of a competent professional person should be sought.

—From a Declaration of Principles jointly adopted by
a Committee of the American Bar Association
and a Committee of Publishers and Associations.

The publisher, editors and authors must disclaim any liability, in whole or in part, arising from the information in this volume. The reader is urged to verify the reference material prior to any detrimental reliance thereupon. Since this material deals with legal, medical and engineering information, the reader is urged to consult with an appropriate licensed professional prior to taking any action that might involve any interpretation or application of information within the realm of a licensed professional practice.

 **Lawyers & Judges
Publishing Company, Inc.**
P.O. Box 30040 • Tucson, AZ 85751-0040
(800) 209-7109 • FAX (800) 330-8795
e-mail: sales@lawyersandjudges.com
www.lawyersandjudges.com

Library of Congress Cataloging-in-Publication Data

Haber, Lyn.
  Challenges to fingerprints / Lyn Haber, Ralph Haber.
    p. cm.
  Includes bibliographical references and index.
  ISBN-13: 978-1-933264-15-8 (softcover : alk. paper)
  ISBN-10: 1-933264-15-2 (softcover : alk. paper)
  1. Fingerprints. 2. Evidence, Criminal--United States. I. Haber, Ralph Norman. II. Title.
  KF9666.5.H33 2009
  363.2'58--dc22

                    2009020608

Printed in the United States of America
10 9 8 7 6 5 4 3 2 1

Contents

Acknowledgments

Several fingerprint examiners reviewed this manuscript. Michele Triplett and David Ashbaugh offered suggestions throughout and at length that changed the book. Boyd Baumgartner generously worked to create the fingerprint images just the way we wanted them, and commented on the text. Allan Bayle and Mark Acree also shared their knowledge and reactions with us. Simon Cole read our text as a researcher and analyst of logical argument, and offered many important suggestions.

Many fingerprint examiners have given enormous amounts of time, patience, and enthusiasm toward teaching us what they actually do, especially Michele Triplett, David Ashbaugh, Kasey Wertheim and Rich Whalley. We benefited from dinner conversations with Glenn Langenburg, John Vanderkolk, and Christophe Champod, and from being yelled at during meetings from the floor by Steve Meagher, Ron Smith, and Alan McRoberts.

We thank our Belinda, whose photographs under-represent her beauty.

We lovingly acknowledge each other. The marriage and partnership survived the intense project of jointly writing this book. It was exciting and it was fun.

Preface

Nearly ten years ago, Ralph asked Lyn an innocent sounding question that had career-changing consequences for both of them. After calculating the error rates in lineup identifications at 50 percent under the best of conditions, Ralph wondered out loud why the courts allow eyewitnesses to testify with their demonstrably high error rates. The courts had been excluding expert testimony on a number of other forensic comparison tasks, including handwriting, polygraphs, and voice identification, primarily because their error rates were unacceptably high.

Then came Ralph's fatal question: "What do you think the error rates are for DNA or fingerprints or firearms?" That did it for Lyn.

Lyn asked if she could spend six months doing nothing but investigating the research on error rates for fingerprints. She chose fingerprint comparisons because there was a 100 year history. She knew little about fingerprints and nothing about how to compare them, but she had 30 years of experience in researching methodology.

She could find no research on error rates, and no evidence to show whether error rates were close to zero, or as bad as eyewitnesses picking out a stranger from a lineup. In the fall of 2001, she presented her search results at a research conference. While there were no fingerprint examiners in the audience, a few weeks later she was called by a lawyer 3,000 miles from that conference who asked for assistance in defending a client whose fingerprint was matched to one found at a crime scene. A month later, she was called by a Federal Defender to provide testimony in a *Daubert* hearing on the admission of fingerprint evidence (*U.S. v. Plaza*, 2002).

Ralph could not resist, and he too got involved in the fingerprint research. He appeared on CBS' *60 Minutes* (Haber, 2003) with a fingerprint examiner (Stephen Meagher) and a Federal Defense lawyer (Robert Epstein), where he described the absence of scientific evidence of the validity of fingerprint comparisons. Lyn and Ralph gave presentations at conferences and wrote articles for journals about the accuracy of comparisons, proficiency and certification testing, quality controls to prevent contamination and bias, and training programs. They interacted with as many examiners in police and sheriff departments' crime laboratories as were willing to spend the time. In the summer of 2002, they jointly signed up for their first latent fingerprint training course, another one in 2003, and a third in 2005. They were taught by superb examiners and teachers. Lawyers continued to call them to solicit expert testimony about fingerprint comparison methodology.

Ralph decided, as a scientist, he wanted to write a large monograph about fingerprint comparison. But he was afraid: "It'll be too long, no one will publish it." Lyn made her fatal mistake. "What about Lawyers & Judges Publishing?" Ralph wrote a proposal and received a contract by return mail, greatly to Lyn's dismay.

Writing a book with someone you eat, sleep and feed the cats with is different from a co-author you can occasionally escape. Ralph writes almost as fast as he speaks, and far less coherently. Lyn needs several hours to write a sentence and even longer to edit one already in place. Their approaches differ as much as their writing styles. The cats heard many complaints about the wrong-headed idiot at the other desk. But after 37 years of professional collaboration, the two Habers know that every disagreement leads to better ideas or clearer expressions of them. They look forward to the next 37 years.

Chapter 1

Introduction to Fingerprints

1.1 A Crime Involving Only Fingerprint Evidence

Two masked men enter a bank, lock the doors, and shout, "This is a robbery!" One man orders everyone to drop to the floor while he remains in the middle of the lobby with a gun. The other robber goes to the front of some of the teller booths, and then back behind them, takes money from each teller's drawer and places the bundles in a paper bag. After about five minutes, the two men run out and disappear from sight.

Investigators arrive within minutes, segregate the witnesses, and interview each one separately. The witnesses said both men's faces were completely covered by the masks. They described the gun variously, none of the witnesses was familiar with guns. They agreed the paper bag was similar to the kind used by most supermarkets, it had some kind of printing. Most witnesses described some of the surfaces touched by the two men.

No suspects were apprehended in the area of the bank immediately afterwards, no snitches reported tips, and no one was found passing any of the marked money that had been stolen.

A crime scene investigator located and lifted a total of 25 usable latent fingerprints from the bank's doors, the counters in front of each teller's booth, and the tellers' drawer handles. (A latent fingerprint is an image of a finger left unintentionally, under uncontrolled conditions.) He found some other latent fingerprints as well, but he judged them too distorted, small or indistinct to be usable, so those he did not lift.

The 25 fingerprint cards were logged into the evidence room of the police station, and then given to Stella Lavie, a latent print examiner in the police crime laboratory. Stella found that the latents were all of fingers (no palms) and all had sufficient detail and clarity to use for comparison. She asked the police to collect rolled fingerprints of the tellers, other bank employees and the investigating officers who might have touched the surfaces on which the latent prints had been found. The police obtained eleven sets of rolled exemplar prints (an exemplar print is a carefully made image on an ideal surface), marked them as elimination prints (taken from persons legitimately present in the bank and therefore already eliminated as suspects), and gave them to Stella.

She compared the 25 crime scene latents to the eleven sets of exemplar prints and was able to identify 20 of the 25 latents to these 11 people licitly in the bank.

The police then gave Stella exemplar prints taken from four suspects in several recent bank robberies, and asked her whether any of them matched the five remaining latent prints. She excluded three of the four suspects, and reported to the police that she could neither identify nor exclude the fourth suspect—there was some similarity, but not enough to make an identification.

In the absence of further suspects, Stella Lavie submitted the five unidentified latent prints to a computer automated fingerprint search system (AFIS), to look for matches from people who had been fingerprinted in the state in the past 30 years. The AFIS was programmed to output the exemplar fingerprints in its database that were most similar to the submitted latent. She asked the AFIS to provide 10 candidates for each latent.

When she compared the first latent to the ten candidate suspects, she identified it to one of them. Similarly, she found that the fourth latent matched one of the candidates generated by the AFIS. She could not find a match for the remaining three latents.

Subsequent police investigation showed that the first of the two identified latent prints from the AFIS search was matched to a customer who had been in the bank earlier on the day of the robbery and who had an alibi at the time of the robbery. The other identified latent matched Mr. Lightfingers, who had previously been convicted of petty theft, which is why he was in the AFIS database. He had no alibi for the time of the bank robbery, and while no gun, bag, mask, or money was found linking him to the crime, and he denied involvement, he was indicted and tried as a defendant on the basis of the single fingerprint match.

At the trial, Stella Lavie testified that she had identified the latent print from the crime scene to Mr. Lightfinger's right index finger. She showed the jury a chart with an enlarged photograph of the latent side by side with an exemplar print of the defendant's right index finger. She pointed out 13 points of correspondence between the two prints, places where each print contained the same fingerprint feature in the same relative location. Stella testified that based on her training and experience, this amount of agreement was sufficient for her to conclude with 100 percent certainty that the latent fingerprint found in the bank was made by the right index finger of the defendant, and could have been made by no other person on earth. As further evidence, she reported that one of her colleagues verified the identification.

Mr. Lightfinger's lawyer asked Stella Lavie whether the print could not have been left by Mr. Lightfingers in the bank at another time. She said, Yes, the match shows only that he touched that surface at some point in time.

The jury found Mr. Lightfingers guilty.

1.2 Critical Issues in this Scenario

- The crime scene investigator chose not to lift some latent fingerprints, because he judged them to be too distorted, small or indistinct to be usable. Is there a standard for this choice? If not lifted, the print disappears forever.
- The crime scene investigator made drawings of the location of the latents. Is this adequate evidence to tie them to the crime scene? Should he have taken photographs?
- Stella Lavie, the fingerprint examiner, decided that the 25 lifted latents had sufficient detail and clarity to use for comparison. What standard did she use to decide?
- Stella was able to identify 20 of the 25 latents to exemplars of people lawfully in the bank. In normal practice, she would know that these 11 sets of exemplars were taken from people not guilty of the crime. Does that prior information bias her judgment?
- In the Automated Fingerprint Search (AFIS) she asked the AFIS to provide 10 candidates for each of the five latent prints. When she compared the candidates and the latents, she was able to identify two of the latents. Are fingerprint comparisons based on an AFIS search handled in the same way as when the police produce the suspect?

- When Stella made an identification, what standard did she use to decide?
- Is a single fingerprint identification based on an AFIS search (which is called a cold hit) enough to indict or convict in the absence of any other evidence of Mr. Lightfinger's involvement in the crime?
- How was Stella Lavie trained? How did she qualify to become a latent fingerprint examiner? What evidence is there of her proficiency?
- Is the crime laboratory in which Stella works accredited? What regulations are in place to assure quality control?

1.3 How Accurate are Fingerprint Comparisons?

Jennifer Mnookin (2007) suggested a thought experiment, in which she asked two of her law students to research the accuracy of identifications based on fingerprint comparisons. She limited the first student's research to judicial opinions that assessed fingerprint conclusions. That hypothetical student, based on a considerable body of judicial decisions, concluded that fingerprint comparisons meet Daubert requirements and are highly reliable evidence.

Like Mnookin's hypothetical student and nearly all judges who have made rulings to admit fingerprint evidence, textbooks and affidavits published by fingerprint examiners typically treat identifications based on fingerprint comparisons as 100 percent certain. These documents provide the essentials of how to compare fingerprints. They focus on the assumptions of the profession and the procedures to be followed. They also claim that the method used to compare fingerprints is very, very accurate—*the method is valid.*

Mnookin asked a second hypothetical student to investigate academic publications about the accuracy of fingerprint comparisons. That student (like Lyn Haber) found that the accuracy of fingerprint evidence is untested. Research scientists and legal scholars have published a number of articles and affidavits on why fingerprint comparison methods fail to meet the scientific requirements now demanded by courts. These publications rarely discuss how to compare fingerprints, but focus on the lack of supporting scientific evidence for the validity of fingerprint comparisons. They typically conclude that because the accuracy of the comparison method has not been proven scientifically, fingerprint evidence should not be admissible in court. If the research scientists are correct, the method used to compare fingerprints may or may not be accurate—its *validity is unknown.*

1.4 About the Authors

We, Lyn and Ralph Haber, have been privileged to interact with and learn from latent fingerprint examiners of incredible skill and dedication who take great pride in their work. We believe, as do they, that they rarely, if ever make an erroneous identification in court. However, we have sat helplessly by in court during the testimony of under-trained, under-informed latent print examiners whose identifications have led to convictions. We believe an unknown number of these identifications are erroneous.

1.5 Fingerprint Examiners and the Organizations that Regulate Them

There are five organizations and their members that constitute a professional fingerprint community in the United States. These are briefly described in Table 1.1.

The National Academy of Sciences in a recent report (NAS, 2009, S-14) recommended that Congress should establish and appropriate funds for an independent federal entity to establish and enforce best practices for forensic professionals and laboratories.

1.6 Who is the Relevant Scientific Community to Evaluate Fingerprint Comparison Methodology for the Courts?

The question of who constitutes the relevant scientific community with respect to fingerprint comparison procedures has confused the courts as well as the profession. Does the relevant community consist of the technicians who perform the comparisons or a group of research scientists and legal scholars who may not be trained in fingerprint comparisons and who do not normally belong to any of the organizations listed in Table 1.1?

Consider a parallel example from a medical comparison: pregnancy testing. Four kinds of technical experts are involved in that testing: the laboratory technician trained to draw the blood sample under uncontaminated conditions, the laboratory technician trained to process the samples so that the hormone is isolated under uncontaminated conditions, the laboratory technician trained to measure the concentration of that hormone and report its amount in specified units, and the laboratory administrator who looks up the amount of concentration in a table and writes a report interpreting that value. While these are all highly trained technicians, they are not research scientists. Two categories of research scientists can testify. The first are the researchers who ran the experiments that demonstrated the relationship between the concentration of the hormone and the probability of pregnancy. The second are other research scientists capable of evaluating the validity of that research.

Table 1.1
Professional Organizations that Represent and
Regulate the Fingerprint Profession

1. The International Association for Identification (IAI) consists of forensic examiners from a range of specialties. Fingerprint examiners comprise the majority of its membership, about 5,000 of its over 7,000 total members. It holds regional meetings and one national meeting. Its many committees meet frequently to work on problems common to the profession. The IAI publishes the *Journal of Forensic Identification*, a journal of research and commentary, and *IDentification News*, another journal on business and approvals of regulations. Its website is www.theiai.org.
2. The American Society of Crime Laboratory Directors (ASCLD) is made up of the directors of over 300 crime laboratories employing fingerprint examiners. The ASCLD provides an umbrella for accreditation of crime laboratories, and supervises proficiency testing, quality controls, training, and rules and regulations. ASCLD publishes its policies in the IAI journals, and on its website: www. ascld.org.
3. The Department of Justice (DOJ), part of the executive branch of America's central government, houses the National Institute of Justice (NIJ). The NIJ overviews the profession, identifies research and staffing needs, and offers some funding for laboratories and research. Its website is www.ojp.usdoj.gov/nij.
4. The Federal Bureau of Investigation (FBI) is housed entirely within the NIJ. The FBI employs the largest crime laboratory of fingerprint examiners in the world, and contains the largest database of fingerprints, over 600 million from 60 million people. The FBI provides training and continuing education for many examiners employed in other laboratories, and its policies and programs serve as models for the rest of the profession.
5. The Scientific Working Group on Friction Ridge Analysis, Study and Technology (SWGFAST) consists of 30 elected members from the above organizations. SWGFAST makes recommendations about regulations and requirements for fingerprint examiners, including education, training, proficiency and certification testing. SWGFAST also makes recommendations to ensure quality control of the laboratories in which examiners work. SWGFAST identifies

continued...

Table 1.1 (continued)

> research needs and cooperates with international and other national organizations. SWGFAST disseminates guidelines, studies and findings through the IAI's journals. Its website is www.swgfast. org.
>
> 6. The National Institute for Forensic Science (NIFS) is a proposed new regulatory and funding federal agency for all of the forensic sciences, including fingerprints. The National Academy of Sciences Report (2009) strongly recommended the immediate creation of NIFS. If carried out by Congress, NIFS will coordinate the proficiency and certification requirements of fingerprint examiners, coordinate the accreditation of crime laboratories in which fingerprint comparisons are carried out, regulate quality assurance and quality control programs, and provide guidelines for research funding. The NIFS is not expected to replace any of the above organizations, but by requiring compliance with their regulatory programs under one umbrella (including comparable ones from the other forensic disciplines), the existence of NIFS will strengthen the fingerprint profession.

With respect to fingerprint comparisons, the relevant scientific community is made up of the researchers who have run scientific experiments establishing the accuracy of the comparison method, and establishing the standards used to justify conclusions based on the method. (Two examples of establishing standards are: the amount and kind of detail required in a latent that make it usable for comparison, and the amount of agreement between the latent and exemplar that ensures an identification.) Fingerprint examiners, like the highly trained technicians in the pregnancy example, carry out procedures that demand training, experience, and skill. However, they are not trained to evaluate the validity of the procedure they use.

1.7 Our Goals and Intended Audience

Our goal is to help the fingerprint profession find more evidence about the accuracy of fingerprint comparison. We hope to help improve the legal system, as it moves toward scientific evaluation of evidence. This book is intended for use by practicing examiners, defense and prosecution lawyers, and specialists in every forensic discipline whose work involves the identification of one single individual or object from a host of possibilities. We address the forensic identification field of fingerprints. Our discussion applies equally to every field of forensic identification—DNA, ballistics, handwriting, footwear, fibers.

Above all, we attempt to bridge the gap between practicing fingerprint examiners and research scientists. This book requires the research scientist to learn a lot about fingerprint comparisons, and the fingerprint examiner to learn a lot about research science. It allows lawyers to learn about both.

We also identify the scientific issues that are unresolved, or un-approached, in the hope that fingerprint examiners will join research scientists to carry out this important, fascinating research.

We explain in explicit ways how the fingerprint profession can strengthen scientific assumptions, methods and documentation. We describe precisely where current scientific requirements by the courts are not met, and how they can be satisfied.

We meld fingerprint comparison and scientific method, so that every step taken, every conclusion offered, and every standard applied in fingerprint comparison can be quantified, measured, and justified on the basis of scientific evidence to ensure it is correct or accurate to a known level of scientific certainty.

1.8 Chapter Outlines

A fingerprint examiner testifies in court: this latent fingerprint matches the right index finger of this individual. In our book, we explore the examiner's conclusion as scientists. We divide the twelve chapters of the book into five main sections.

The first section, including this chapter and Chapters 2 and 3, provides the background for forensic fingerprint comparison. We discuss the assumptions necessary to identify, or match, a latent print to a single finger (Chapter 2). These assumptions are more numerous and more complex than they first appear. Suppose we grant from the outset that the pattern of skin on every finger is unique and remains constant over the finger's lifetime. This does not mean that the fingerprint examiner could match a crime scene latent to your finger (assuming you are the true perpetrator). You did not leave your finger at the crime, just a latent print—a two-dimensional, tiny, blurred image of your finger. How unique are the patterns in the latent? We describe differences among fingers, controlled, good images of fingers, and uncontrolled latent prints, and the features used to compare fingerprints (Chapter 3).

The second section reviews the process of fingerprint comparison. We start with the acquisition of latent fingerprints at a crime scene and the processing of prints in the crime laboratory (Chapter 4). We then present in detail the comparison method called ACE that fingerprint examiners employ when they compare two fingerprints (Chapter 5). In Chapter 6 we describe the procedures used when no suspect is available and the crime scene latent print is submitted to an automated computer search system.

The third section of the book addresses the accuracy of conclusions reached by fingerprint examiners applying the ACE method. Accurate conclusions depend on both the proficiency of individual examiners, and on the accuracy of the method itself. Chapter 7 describes and evaluates the proficiency testing programs for fingerprint examiners. Chapter 8 reviews evidence of the accuracy of individual examiners and of the ACE method, independent of examiner errors.

The fourth section concerns sources of bias and error, and professional regulations and standards that govern quality control. A director of a crime laboratory wants to assure the highest quality (most accurate) work product possible. What controls does he put in place? We outline the kinds of contaminants that can bias the work of fingerprint examiners in Chapter 9, and how quality controls can contain or prevent these biases. In Chapter 10, we focus on regulations governing the professional qualifications of the personnel and of the crime laboratory itself.

In the fifth section, we return to the crevasse between the fingerprint profession and scientific researchers. In Chapter 11 we review the defense offered by the fingerprint profession in response to challenges about the accuracy of the ACE method. In Chapter 12 we review the challenges to fingerprints that we have raised throughout the book: questions whose answers are unknown today, but can be discovered through experimental research.

Chapter 2

Individualization: Fingerprint Comparison Is Not Like Finding Your Wife in a Crowd

In everyday life, you identify familiar objects and people all the time. Many dogs live the world over, but your dog Lola is an individual, not to be confused with any other dog. To identify Lola, you have to be able to tell individual dogs apart. If you could not individualize, you could not find your own home, your spouse, or your dog. People do make occasional embarrassing mistakes, such as when you call to your wife across the parking lot: "Honey, I'm right here!" and when the woman turns around, she is a stranger.

When you identify someone, you can do it because they are familiar. You do not claim expertise, special training, or that you are using a scientific method.

A latent fingerprint examiner such as Stella Lavie, working on the bank robbery described in Chapter 1, compares two unfamiliar fingerprints, the first from an unknown donor, the second from a known suspect, and decides whether one single finger or two different fingers made the two prints. Everyday speech has multiple names for this process: identify, match, individuate, individualize, recognize. Stella Lavie is able to compare these unfamiliar prints because she was trained to follow a scientific method, and has practiced comparisons following this method until she could perform in accordance with the standards of the profession. She has become an expert.

The two kinds of identification, your familiar Lola, and an unfamiliar fingerprint, are vastly different comparison processes. They differ in the familiarity of the objects being compared, and they differ in whether the person doing the comparison is an expert following a scientific method.

2.1 Everyday (Non-Forensic) Individualization

Imagine you are attending a black tie affair of some thousands of people. Emerging from an outside balcony where you had withdrawn for respite, you glance down looking for your wife in the throng. Your task is to individuate: you are looking for one single individual, Rosie, and no other among the thousands. This is possible only if Rosie's appearance is *unique*, no one else at the party looks quite the same as she does. Her characteristics also must be *permanent* over time. Finally, and most important, your wife must be highly *familiar* to you.

To identify Rosie, you use a template or a generalized representation that has been built up in your memory over the multiple times you have viewed your wife. If you were asked to describe this template to someone who does not know your wife, you would discover how vague your representation is. Your template does not depend on knowing a set of individual features, or even remembering the particular clothes or hairdo she's wearing that evening (Peterson and Rhodes, 2003). It's not a single view of your wife, it's a composite "Rosie-ness." Your template of her is different from everyone else's, because it is the product of your individual experiences in perceiving Rosie. It is an experiential-based expertise, built up over years of practice and improvement. And over years of corrective feedback. You find out fast when you've made a mistake!

If Rosie is visible in the melee at the gala, her template "pops out" in your awareness. It is a sudden, automatic, unconscious process that does not require a method, or thought, or a stepwise comparison. This description is the essence of what is meant by familiar.

2.2 Forensic Individualization

Perceptual scientists are confident that you use an entirely different process when you compare two *unfamiliar* people or objects or fingerprints to individuate one to the other (Tanaka and Farah, 2003). Table 2.1 describes the critical differences between identification of familiar objects and individuating unfamiliar stimuli.

Table 2.1
Six Differences Between Individuating Familiar and Unfamiliar Targets

Template vs. Two Unfamiliar Targets
Your memory of your wife is a composite, or a template, so you can identify your wife each time you see her, regardless of which manifestation of her occurs. (A manifestation is her appearance at a single, specific time.) The template is, in a sense, the underlying perceptual memory essence of your wife.

A finger, like your wife, has infinite manifestations. Every touch of a finger on a surface leaves a different version of the friction ridge skin pattern. The examiner sees only the two, unfamiliar images that are frozen under his magnifying glass. In order to identify the latent, he has to *compare that single, unfamiliar image to a different, unfamiliar single image.*

Memory vs. Vision Source
In everyday life, you have a holistic *memory* of familiar people and objects. When you attempt to individuate an unfamiliar object, as in forensic fingerprint comparison, you have to use features you can see right now. The fingerprint examiner has no memory for unfamiliar fingerprints he's never encountered before, but must rely on what he can see when he looks at the prints.

continued...

Table 2.1 (continued)

Template vs. Describable Features
With unfamiliar images there is no template. The examiner must use *visible, describable characteristics* to compare the two fingerprints, in the same way you would to decide whether the two images in Figure 2.1 are of the same woman.

Template vs. Spatial Locations of Features
Generalized features represented in memory lack a specific spatial referent. Because the fingerprints are unfamiliar, to compare the two fingerprints, the examiner must assign *specific spatial locations* to every feature in the fingerprint.

Automatic vs. Conscious Attention
The holistic template you use when you identify familiar people pops up in memory instantaneously and automatically, without conscious effort. Human brains are wired to identify familiar objects (Peterson and Rhodes, 2003). In contrast, forensic identification requires *conscious attention* to guide the comparison process and conclusions.

Automatic vs. Step-by-Step Method
This conscious attention is applied to a *specified method* to carry out the comparison. The framework of the method has three components: an *analysis* of the target, the latent fingerprint that includes a complete description of its features in their spatial locations; a *comparison* of the features-in-place in the unknown and known, as in the latent and in an exemplar; and an *evaluation* of the amount of similarity between the two that leads to a conclusion. Underlying the conclusion is a set of standards on which that conclusion is based. How much similarity is enough for a given conclusion, such as identification?

2.3 Experiential Feedback and Scientific Method

Charlie was a foreman in a large shop that repaired electrical appliances, back in the days when individual failed components were repaired or replaced, rather than throwing the entire vacuum cleaner or fan away. Repairmen working under Charlie considered him a wizard, because he could listen to the appliance and diagnose the problem.

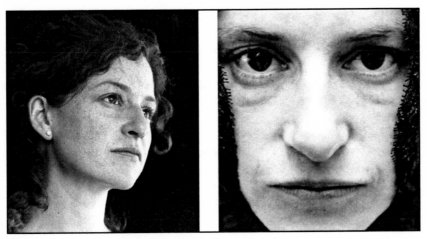

Figure 2.1 *A pair of photographs of women who may or may not be the same person.*

Charlie spent years repairing electrical appliances. Every time he identified the failed component by sound, he opened up the vacuum or fan and discovered ground truth: he could see that his diagnosis was right, and fix the appliance. On the rare occasions when he was wrong, he could immediately see ground truth, reevaluate his diagnosis, and improve his diagnostic skills so he did not make the same mistake again. Feedback on each trial enabled Charlie to develop his wizard ears, he was not born with them. Charlie's ability was *experienced based*, slowly built up over a lifetime, and always supported by immediate feedback. Charlie knows he's extremely accurate, and that accuracy is confirmed by immediate feedback on his accuracy. However, he is not applying a specified method that would let him train another appliance repair foreman.

Imagine a task comparable to a forensic one. A police officer is shown many paired different photographs of unfamiliar women and he is asked, for each pair, whether the two women are the same person (see Figure 2.1). The two photographs in each pair may be taken from different distances, different viewpoints, with differing expressions, context and clothing. But are they the same woman? To answer, the officer visually compares the two photographs: the individual features of each face, each in their spatial relationships to each other. The officer knows to ignore irrelevant differences such as context, orientation, expression, and clothing.

Suppose he is told the correct answer (ground truth) right after he makes each decision. With feedback, like Charlie, he can improve his comparison skills. If ground truth is unknown, or he receives no feedback after each answer, even years of experience may not improve his accuracy. Without information about his conclusions in relation to ground truth, there's no way for him to know if he's even getting better at individuating faces.

This is the case with most forensic individualization casework tasks. Ground truth is often unknown, and Stella Lavie seldom knows whether her answer is correct. Feedback is replaced by training to use a scientific, valid method. Stella can have some confidence that she's correct when she testifies in court on a particular case, even without knowing its ground truth, because the method she follows has a demonstrated accuracy, and Stella herself has a demonstrated proficiency in applying the method.

In the remainder of this chapter, we consider the underlying assumptions and characteristics of a scientific method that can bolster an examiner's confidence even without feedback on the accuracy of her testimony.

2.4 The Fingerprint Examiner's Task

Stella Lavie's task is the following. Her supervisor hands her an unknown crime scene latent fingerprint and George's exemplar fingerprint that was made in the police station last night and asks whether the two prints match. The scientific accuracy of her conclusion is demonstrated by how well the method allows her to sort pairs of fingerprints into two separate piles based on whether each pair truly shares or does not share the same underlying pattern. To get from a conclusion of identical underlying patterns to a conclusion of a single donor also requires a uniqueness assumption: no two people share the same patterns on their fingers. We describe uniqueness assumptions later in this chapter.

A. Assessment of Sorting Accuracy When the Target Stimuli are Never Confusable: Ants and Elephants

Imagine a zoologist who stumbles upon a previously unexplored island. She discovers two new creatures there, and she wants to describe how they differ. She decides to use a method to differentiate them based on their height. Using her measuring stick (which her careful experiments have demonstrated can differentiate height with an error of measurement less than one-quarter inch), she plots her height data, as shown in Figure 2.2. Her method works. Height measurements sort these creatures into two groups, one of creatures who measure less than one foot in height, and a second one of creatures who exceed six feet.

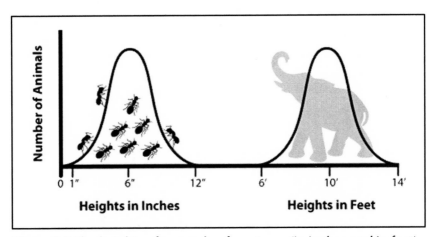

Figure 2.2 *The heights of a sample of creatures (in inches and in feet) measured on an unexplored island.*

When the zoologist encounters a native expert, she's given independent measures of ground truth based on tusks and number of legs. (Ground truth is absolute knowledge of the true classification of each individual.) Her height method predicts perfectly: no ants have been mixed up in the elephant category, and no elephants have been included in the ant category. She can choose a variety of threshold standards to reach her conclusions, anywhere from 1 foot 1/4 inches to 5 feet 3/4 inches, and any one of those threshold standards perfectly predicts in which category an individual creature belongs. The target stimuli never overlap. Her method can differentiate between ants and elephants with 100 percent accuracy, because her method's procedure is accurate plus or minus 1/4 inches, and the target stimuli she is comparing differ by a minimum of more than 4 feet. What a lucky zoologist!

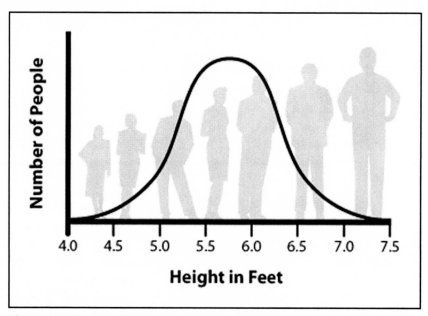

Figure 2.3 *The height measurements of a sample of people (in feet) measured in America.*

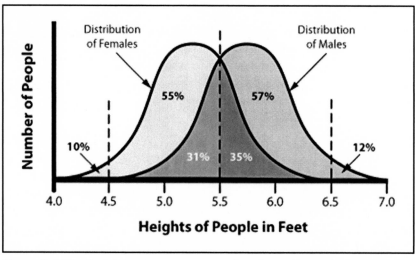

Figure 2.4 *The height measurements, taken from Figure 3, separated into female and male categories, with a threshold standard of 5.5 ft. The percentage of each sex above and below the threshold standard is shown.*

B. Assessment of Sorting Accuracy When the Target Stimuli are Confusable: Sex

As a different example, an extremely naive anthropologist comes to the United States to study the difference between men and women. He needs a method to differentiate between the two sexes. He heard how well the zoologist's method worked for ants and elephants, and decides to use it. He measures the height of a random sample of adults (containing no dwarves) and discovers that the shortest members in his sample are just below 4.5 feet, and the tallest are 7.5 feet (see Figure 2.3).

Where should he place his threshold standard to separate the sexes when he found no discontinuity in heights? When his measurements are compared to knowledge of ground truth (obtained in a more conventional way), as shown in Figure 2.4, he observes that everyone shorter than 4.5 feet is female, and everyone taller than 6.5 feet is male.

Height does differentiate between the sexes when the scores are very small or very large. But in the middle range, where most of his sample is located, some people are male and some are female at each height, and height does not predict sex 100 percent accurately for most of the people in his sample.

The anthropologist made a stab at locating a threshold standard. He needed one that would declare members of his sample as male or female, even without known ground truth. The best he could do was 5.5 feet, which as can be seen, does not differentiate sex very well. The percentages of males and females are marked in Figure 2.4. The height measurements of females predict sex accurately 65 percent of the time (10 percent + 55 percent), and misclassify women 35 percent of the time. For males, height predicts sex accurately 69 percent of the time (57 percent + 12 percent). If the threshold standard is set higher or lower than 5.5 feet, the percentage of erroneous sex identifications increases, so 5.5 feet is the best threshold to use.

Unlike differentiation of ants and elephants, height is not a good method to use to predict sex, because the method produces overlapping distributions: men and women in this example can have the same height 78 percent of the time. (If you doubt the reasonableness of this example, see Dabbs, 2009). The method of height measurement lacks *validity:* conclusions based on this method frequently do not match ground truth.

C. Assessment of Sorting Accuracy for Fingerprints: Are Same and Different Underlying Patterns Confusable?

A fingerprint examiner's task resembles the zoologist's and anthropologist's. The comparison method assesses the amount of similarity in the patterns in the two prints, and then provides a threshold standard to sort the pairs of fingerprints into two categories: one for the same finger made them (ant-ant, elephant-elephant; both female, both male), and the other for different fingers made them (ant-elephant, male-female). If the examiner's method always finds a lot of similarity between two fingerprint patterns from a single finger, and very little similarity for two patterns in prints from two different fingers, the data look like elephants and ants (Figure 2.2) and the method that permitted that sorting is highly accurate. If, when there's a moderate amount of overlap in the similarity scores, the method cannot discriminate, the data look like adult heights as a function of sex (Figure 2.4). Then the method fails to distinguish accurately whether the two prints came from one finger or two.

1. Exemplar prints

Figure 2.5 shows four exemplar fingerprints taken from the same finger. Because they were made carefully and under controlled conditions, they are quite similar. However, because the surface skin of fingers is flexible and squishy, the friction ridge pattern in each exemplar is never identical. While the underlying friction ridge pattern on the finger remains the same, the pattern in each print of the finger varies. Every finger, like multiple photographs of your wife, has many representations.

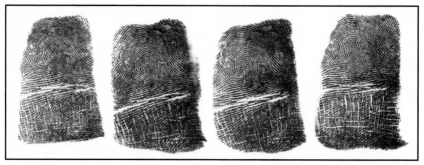

Figure 2.5 *Four exemplar fingerprints made from the same finger.*

It's unknown how accurately a fingerprint comparison method compares exemplar fingerprints to one another. Can the method always sort exemplars taken from the same finger into one pile, and exemplars taken from different fingers into a different pile? We consider some evidence below.

2. Latent prints

The friction ridge pattern in a latent print is not always clear. Simplistically, the underlying pattern fails to be represented in two ways: some information is missing altogether (a quantity measure), and some is ambiguous (a quality measure). Imagine a latent in which only three features are visible, but they are very clear. How many different exemplars could this latent match? Surely, more than one. Now imagine the same latent, but the three features are indistinct: maybe there's a ridge ending, maybe not; maybe that's a bifurcation, maybe not. This latent could be matched to an even larger number of exemplars, because feature #1 in the latent matches an exemplar with a ridge ending in that location, *and* it matches an exemplar with a continuous ridge. Latent prints, like any unclear stimuli, can be *confusable*. They may match multiple larger, clearer patterns. This suggests that poor quality latents, like middle range heights, are consistent with multiple ground truths.

If poorer quality latents are confusable, a method to compare fingerprints needs to sort pairs of prints into at least four piles. Two are the same as described for the exemplar-to-exemplar comparison: a same source pile (identification) and a different source pile (exclusion). A third pile contains pairs in which the latent print is too impoverished in quality or quantity to be used to compare (examiners call this no value). The fourth pile contains pairs in which the latent print member of the pair is of value, with patterns consistent with the exemplar, but there is not enough information either to identify or exclude (examiners call this category insufficient or inconclusive).

How does the profession discover whether latents are confusable? How does the method describe which characteristics to use to sort the latents? We answer these questions in Chapter 5. How accurately does the method match a latent to the correct exemplar? We describe some evidence below.

2.5 Assumptions for Forensic Fingerprint Comparisons

Forensic fingerprint comparison requires the assumption that the patterns on fingers be permanent over time. Otherwise, there would not be any point in comparing them.

Individualization on the basis of friction ridge pattern requires also that the pattern be unique. No other finger has the same pattern. Otherwise, an examiner could never conclude with certainty that George made this fingerprint, because Ralph might have made the same one.

A. The Permanence Assumption for Friction Ridge Skin Patterns

Two kinds of evidence support the assumption that friction ridge patterns are permanent. The first comes from research on the generation of friction ridge skin. The skin on the fingers, palms, toes and soles sloughs off and is replaced roughly every 30 days over every person's lifetime, but the generating layer in the epidermis reproduces the same surface pattern in each regeneration (Babler, 1991; discussed by Wertheim and Maceo, 2003).

The second kind of evidence is based on empirical comparisons of finger-prints taken from the same person over large gaps of time (Galton, 1892). The results suggest that exemplar prints taken at different times in a person's life are highly similar.

For both reasons, the permanence of friction ridge skin patterns is generally accepted by the fingerprint profession, by forensic scientists and by the courts.

B. The Uniqueness Assumptions for Friction Ridge Skin Patterns

Embedded in the uniqueness assumption are further necessary propositions. (1) If the patterns in an *exemplar* match those on George's *fingers*, George made the exemplar, an exemplar to finger assertion. (2) If the patterns in an *unknown exemplar* match those in a *known exemplar* from George, George made the unknown exemplar, an exemplar to exemplar claim. (3) If the patterns in an *unknown latent* match those in a *known exemplar* from George, George made the latent, a latent to exemplar claim. In each case, the unknown print can be used to conclude that George's finger made them—he is the donor source.

We review the research and statistical evidence to support these uniqueness assumptions.

1. Uniqueness of patterns on fingers

Most people believe the old wives' tale that nature never repeats herself. The pattern of every snowflake is unique, the pattern of every leaf is unique, and the friction ridge pattern on every finger is unique. Like many an old wives' tale it may well be true; but stated in this form, it is unprovable. It is impossible to compare every finger of every dead, living and yet unborn person. However, the statistical implications of scientific research on the development of these patterns during gestation support this assumption very convincingly.

Embryological research on the development of friction ridges has demon-strated that they are formed in different ways depending on the *shape* of the volar pads on the hands and feet during prenatal development and on the *timing* of their growth (Babler, 1991). The research shows that some of the determinants of the shape of the pads, combined with the timing of their growth, are *random processes*. Scientists generally accept that random, complex processes produce unique consequences with astronomically high probability (Ashbaugh, 1999, p. 73; Aitken, 1995).

The statistical arguments supporting the uniqueness of friction ridge sys-tems on fingers have been generally accepted, by the fingerprint profession, by researchers and by the courts.

2. Uniqueness of patterns in exemplar fingerprints

The uniqueness assumption requires that the patterns in every exemplar from the same finger differ from the patterns in exemplars made by every other finger. Two kinds of shaky evidence have been offered.

a. Failure to find repeated patterns

One kind of evidence is anecdotal and based on a lack of evidence: no examiner has ever published an example of the same pattern of friction ridge skin from exemplars of two different fingers. Since it is likely that the discovery of such an example would be published immediately, the absence of publication is treated as evidence that no exemplars share the same pattern. Fingerprint texts usually quote this argument (Champod et al., 2004, is an exception) and it is mentioned in many trials when uniqueness of the patterns used in fingerprint comparison is challenged.

Challenge

Success in finding two exemplars with the same pattern depends on fingerprint examiners having a perfect memory for every exemplar they have ever seen, a memory extending over years. Memory research has shown that such memory demands are impossible (Haber and Haber, 2000). This argument is fundamentally flawed and offers no support for the uniqueness of exemplar fingerprints.

b. Computer comparisons of pairs of exemplar fingerprints

Another approach to show that exemplars from different sources do not share the same patterns has used a computer search system to compare pairs of exemplar prints for their similarity. The hope in such a study would be results like the height data in Figure 2.2. Two different exemplars made from the same finger (mated prints) should always produce high similarity scores (like the elephant-elephant and ant-ant comparisons), and two exemplars made from two different fingers should produce low similarity scores (ants-elephants). This procedure has been tried twice.

Using a U.S. National Institute for Standards and Technology (NIST) database consisting of two sets of different tenprint exemplars taken from 2,700 individuals (54,000 prints), Cole et al. (2008) selected a subset of 6,750 mated prints. An AFIS system compared them to the remaining different prints in the database. Each search produced 10 candidates. The AFIS algorithm assigned each candidate a "match score" indicating its similarity to the input exemplar. The authors found that the true match (mate) had the highest similarity score (and appeared as the top candidate) 75 percent of the time. The true match ranked among the other 9 candidates 4 percent of the time. The remaining 21 percent of the time, the true match was not included in the top ten candidates. Conversely, they found that AFIS produced some non-matches with very high similarity scores as the top candidate, and other non-matches ranked among the remaining candidates.

The results show that some exemplars ranked as the top matching candidate, or receiving very high differential scores between the top candidate and the averaged scores ranked 2-10, are false matches: they are more similar to exemplars from a different individual than to a different exemplar made from the same finger. To the extent that these data would be found if human examiners performed the comparisons, the exemplar-to-exemplar uniqueness assumption fails.

Challenge

This study employed a computer system, not human examiners, so it is uninformative about human comparison accuracy. The system, unlike most automated systems in general use, analyzed the submitted latent using its own algorithms (many systems require a human technician to preprocess the latent for submission, see Chapter 6). Because these processing and similarity algorithms are proprietary, it is unlikely that the results of this study can be generalized to other automated search systems.

The Cole et al. study serves a very important function in the fingerprint world: it has been performed correctly, replacing an oft-quoted, improperly conducted, unpublished demonstration produced as part of a Daubert hearing on the admissibility of fingerprint evidence (Meagher, Budowle and Ziesig, 1998). Meagher et al. used an AFIS system to compare 50,000 exemplars with themselves, not a second take of the same finger. This was an *identity* comparison. The algorithms in the AFIS search discriminated, with astronomical accuracy, between exemplars that were identical and those that were not. This study is irrelevant to the claim that two different exemplars from the same finger can always be matched to each other, and not to any other exemplar.

Challenge

At present, there is no research evidence to support a uniqueness assumption for exemplar fingerprints.

Challenge

Cole et al. (2008) and Cole (2009) correctly observe that uniqueness by itself does not assure that an examiner will perceive critical subtle (or even molecular) differences among images of friction ridge skin patterns, especially because the flexibility of the skin creates differences in every impression. Therefore, uniqueness of friction ridge skin is insufficient for individualization: the extent to which pattern variations from different donors appear indistinguishable from variations within a single donor must be included in estimating the probability of error.

3. Uniqueness of patterns in latent fingerprints

The latent to exemplar uniqueness assumption requires that if a latent print can be matched to George's exemplar, George made the latent. The pattern in a latent print must be unique, so it only matches exemplars made by the single, true donor finger.

a. Computer comparisons of latent to exemplar prints

Cole et al. (2008) used their AFIS to determine whether a latent and an exemplar from the same finger would always have a higher similarity score than a latent and exemplar from different fingers. The NIST database in their second study contained 258 latent-exemplar pairs, which were different takes of the same finger. The authors found that the true exemplar match for the latent was ranked as the top candidate 70 percent of the time, and was ranked among the other nine candidates 12 percent of the time. The candidate list failed to contain the correct exemplar about 18 percent of the time.

Again, the results for latent to exemplar similarity do not resemble Figure 2.2. The authors reported that all the false matches received a higher score than the lowest scoring true match. Thirty-four percent of the true matches scored lower than the highest scoring false match. These data suggest that the uniqueness hypothesis fails for latent to exemplar comparisons.

Cole et al. (2008) corrected the erroneous procedures and conclusions offered by Meagher et al. (1998) in the second part of their demonstration. The latter manufactured "latents" by masking off all but the center 21.7 percent of the 50,000 exemplars (the FBI's estimate of the average size of a latent), and submitted them to AFIS for comparison with the original 50,000 exemplars from which they had been copied. The AFIS system matched "latent" to exemplar identities with astronomical accuracy. These results cannot be offered as evidence that latent fingerprints are unique, and can be matched to only the exemplar of the finger that made them, because no latent prints were tested. Latent fingerprints are not masked-off centers of identical exemplar fingerprints. A latent print of a finger is a different image of the finger, not an identical one; latents rarely contain the information-rich center; and usually their quality is far poorer than that of the exemplar.

Neither Cole et al. (2008) nor we present these data as representative of results from human examiners making comparisons between normal casework latents and tenprints. Human examiners presumably use different comparison algorithms than an AFIS. The quality of the latents in these experiments is unquantified, and corresponds to casework latents to an unknown extent.

Challenge

No adequate experimental results have been published to support the basic assumptions that different takes of exemplar and latent fingerprints can be correctly matched back to other images from the same finger, and only to images from the same finger. To quote the National Academy of Sciences Report (2009, p. 5-13): "Uniqueness does not guarantee that prints from two different people are always sufficiently different that they cannot be confused, or that two impressions made by the same finger will also be sufficiently similar to be discerned as coming from the same source. The impression left by a given finger will differ every time, because of inevitable variations in pressure, which change the degree of contact between each part of the ridge structure and the impression medium. None of these variables—of features across a population of fingers or of repeated impressions left by the same finger—has been characterized, quantified, or compared."

Challenge

No research has been performed to determine how much ridge pattern, how sharp the detail, and/or how many features must be present in a latent fingerprint for the probability of an identification to an incorrect exemplar to approach zero. Conversely, nothing is known about the probability that a latent of poor quality can be identified to more than one exemplar.

The available data, based on AFIS algorithms ranking similarity, suggest that both the exemplar to exemplar and latent to exemplar uniqueness assumptions fail, with an unknown but sizable probability. These experiments need to be replicated using highly skilled human examiners, to provide evidence of these probabilities. Until those probabilities are known for fingerprint examiners, the use of latent fingerprint evidence in court to identify one and only one donor as the person who left the latent print is not supportable (Haber and Haber, 2007).

2.6 Assessment of the Accuracy (Validity) of Fingerprint Comparison Judgments

The accuracy of the expert opinion proffered by the latent fingerprint examiner depends upon the proficiency of the examiner in applying the comparison method, and on the power of the method to produce correct conclusions when properly applied. Scores obtained on a validated proficiency test containing test materials comparable in type and difficulty to normal casework assess the proficiency of fingerprint examiners.

The power of the method to produce correct conclusions is assessed by demonstration of the method's validity. In science, validity refers to the accuracy of conclusions based on the method, compared with ground truth (knowledge of the true state of the facts: whether the two prints were made by one donor or two donors). The validity of the method to compare fingerprints is the accuracy of conclusions reached by fingerprint examiners who are fully trained and experienced in using the method, comparing latent-exemplar pairs typical of casework but for which ground truth is known (one donor versus two), working under optimal conditions. Any errors made under these circumstances would result from failures of the method itself to produce the correct decision as to one or two donors. Errors could not be attributed to poor proficiency of the examiners doing the comparisons or to poor working conditions. The validity of a method is usually reported as the converse of its accuracy—as an error rate. If the experiment just described showed that the method results in correct conclusions 95 percent of the time, the method's error rate would be 5 percent.

A. Science Differentiates between Reliability and Validity

If highly trained and experienced examiners applied the fingerprint comparison method to compare a large number of latent-exemplar pairs and they all reached the same conclusion about each pair, the method would be shown to be reliable. Also, if the same examiners, years later, compared the same latent-exemplar pairs and each examiner reached the same conclusions about each pair as before, the method would be shown to be reliable. Reliability refers to consistency among the examiners applying the method: they agree with one another, and they make the same judgments over time.

A reliable method is not necessarily valid. Suppose these examiners all reached the same but wrong conclusions. The method would be reliable, but invalid. Most knowledgeable people used their vision to opine that the world was flat (a reliable conclusion), though they were wrong (vision alone can lead to invalid conclusions). If a method is unreliable, so that different examiners reach different conclusions about the same latent-exemplar pair, the method is necessarily invalid, because some of those examiners are reaching the wrong conclusion.

B. A Scientific Method to Compare Fingerprints

Fingerprint examiners today use the Analysis-Comparison-Evaluation method (ACE). A verification stage is sometimes added, in which another examiner repeats the comparison. When that step is added, the method is called ACE-V. (We describe ACE in detail in Chapter 5.) The acronym is taken from a very general comparison framework. It was described initially by Huber (1959) to cover a variety of forensic comparison tasks, including fingerprints. Huber argued that in all forensic comparison disciplines, the examiner analyzes the unknown-source target stimulus which was made in an uncontrolled fashion, then compares that stimulus to the known exemplar stimulus, and evaluates how much similarity is found, and whether it is sufficient to conclude a common origin of the two stimuli.

A general framework is not a comparison method. It becomes a method when the details (wherein reside the devils) for each step are described. For example, in the analysis stage, what do you do to analyze the unknown latent? In what order do you perform each step? When have you completed a sufficient analysis, so you can proceed to compare? What standards do you use for each decision you make?

The fingerprint profession asserts that forensic fingerprint comparison uses a science based methodology (SWGFAST, 2002a). Table 2.2 lists seven requirements for a scientific method for fingerprint comparison.

Table 2.2
Components of a Scientific Fingerprint Comparison Method

- The method is quantitative and specified
- The method has a known error rate
- Objective description of features-in-place
- Objective standards for conclusions
- Objective Measures of latent difficulty
- Protection from bias
- Training and proficiency testing programs

1. The method is quantitative and specified

Quantitative means that each step of the method is fully described and objective. This allows the method's application to be *reliable*. If I ask a number of people to estimate the distance from here to a particular star we can all see, using miles, the estimates will vary a lot, because estimating is not a quantitative method, even though a mile is a quantitative term. When a method is not quantitative, scientists expect the results to be inconsistent and variable.

Suppose I want to cook some lamb shanks. My grandmother made them, fabulously, and has generously given me her recipe. Here it is: coat shanks with flour, braise them in oil with onions, add salt, pepper, potatoes, tomatoes, celery, broth, fresh lemon and seasonings. Cook until done. This is an example of an unquantitative method.

Contrast the next recipe for the same dish: coat 4 lamb shanks with flour. Shake off extra flour. Heat 3 tablespoons oil in 4 quart dutch oven, uncovered, medium high, until very hot (an onion sizzles). Add 1 coarsely sliced onion and shanks, brown shanks 5 minutes per side on all sides. Remove from heat, discard oil. Add 2 cups beef broth, 1 teaspoon salt, 1/2 teaspoon fresh ground pepper, 8 new potatoes, contents of 1 one-pound can of whole tomatoes, etc. Now the method is quantitative.

When a method is quantified, you can measure each of its components. Take salt in the two lamb recipes: in the unquantitative version, you do not know how much to use, or how much I used when you like my lamb shanks. In the objective version, you know exactly how much to use, a teaspoon. Objective means that someone else can look over your shoulder and check whether you measured correctly, and that someone else, measuring the salt or examining the latent, would use the same amount of salt or agree on the presence of a detail in the latent.

A scientific method also defines the order in which steps are taken. Your supervisor could test whether you followed the correct sequence: did you braise the shanks before you added the salt? At each step during the application of the method, the chef or the examiner can describe exactly what he did, so someone else could do it just the same way.

Using the unquantitative method, the resulting dish is different every time, whether I make it or someone else does. The unquantified method is unreliable. In contrast, a quantitative method results in the same dish every time, whether I make it or someone else does, because the method is reliable. With respect to fingerprint comparison, the purpose of a quantified method is to insure that every examiner follows the same procedure every time, so every examiner arrives at the same answer for the same comparison. The quantified method also insures that a comparison can be repeated with the same result. This means the results are reliable.

Suppose you are an arborist and you intend to publish your extensive research that shows that a particular kind of pine tree, long thought to be a single specie, is in fact two. If you simply stated your conclusion, scientists would not pay much attention. They want to know the data you used, the research you carried out, and how you reached your conclusion. In a scientific method, this documentation is required at each step of the way.

This same requirement holds for a method to compare fingerprints. However, fingerprint examiners today generally are not required to record the steps they took, what they saw, or why their comparison was an identification. They report only their conclusion. If a supervisor is to check the accuracy of an examiner's work and only the final outcome is available to him, he cannot determine whether the examiner followed the ACE method correctly. In court, no one can evaluate the steps or procedures the examiner used, because he has not kept a record of them. He can describe how he generally compares two prints, but he cannot detail his work in the instant case. This is comparable to the arborist who failed to report his research, or to a policeman who testifies that the suspect is surely guilty, but he does not recall the specific evidence that demonstrates his guilt.

2. The method has a known error rate

When a method is fully described, it can be experimentally tested to see how well it works—or, conversely, the probability that its conclusions will be wrong. In technical terms, the experiment establishes the *method's error rate.* What is the probability that Rosemary really is pregnant when the outcome of the test says she's not (a missed identification)? What is the probability that she is not pregnant, when the test outcome was positive (an erroneous identification)? Courts want assurance that the method employed has a known accuracy rate. If I, as an expert, testify that Rosemary Roland was pregnant, I must be able to present evidence that the method I used to determine whether she was pregnant gives the right answer. How good is my method? The answer comes from research experiments, in which Rosemary's true state (and a large sample of other women's) is known by the main experimenter, but *not* known by the experimenter who tests for pregnancy or who scores the data. Each woman is tested to see whether she is pregnant. The test can give two kinds of right answers and two kinds of wrong answers. These are shown in Table 2.3.

Table 2.3
Results of a Pregnancy Test as a Function of Ground Truth

Test Results	Ground Truth	
	Pregnant	**Not Pregnant**
Positive Test	Correct	Erroneous Identification
Negative Test	Missed Identification	Correct

If the pregnancy test method were perfectly accurate, all of the results would fall in the left-to-right downward diagonal of Table 2.3: the test would show Yes Pregnant when the women actually were pregnant, and Not Pregnant when they truly were not. The data would look exactly like the height sorts for ants and elephants shown in Figure 2.2.

Scientific tests do not reach perfection. Instead, experts must present the *error rate* of the methods they employ: the percent of time the method reaches the wrong conclusion, even when applied just the right way. In Table 2.3, two kinds of errors can occur, shown in the upward left-to-right diagonal of the Table. The first kind, a *missed identification,* refers to the percent of time the method misses a pregnancy. The test showed the woman not pregnant when she really was. The second kind of error, *an erroneous identification*, occurs when the test shows the woman is pregnant, but she really is not.

Table 2.4

Results of a Fingerprint Comparison Test as a Function of Ground Truth

Comparison Results	Ground Truth	
	One Donor	Two Donors
Identification	Correct	Erroneous Identification
Exclusion	Missed Identification	Correct

Suppose I am a fingerprint examiner. I examine a latent print from a crime scene by comparing it to a fingerprint from a suspect. The kinds of outcomes of this test, shown in Table 2.4, are identical to Table 2.3.

If the comparison test were perfectly accurate, all of the results would fall on the left-to-right downward diagonal of Table 2.4. The test would show Yes when the perpetrator and the suspect were the same, and No when the perpetrator was not the suspect. The question for the legal system is, what is the probability that the fingerprint examiner made a mistake? Looking at the first entry in the second line in Table 2.4, if the examiner says the perpetrator is not the suspect when in fact he is, a guilty criminal goes free. If the examiner says the suspect is the perpetrator, when he truly is not, an innocent person is identified as the perpetrator—an erroneous identification (the second entry in the first line in the Table). How often does this happen in the real world? We discuss the available but inadequate evidence for error rate in Chapter 8.

3. Objective description of features-in-place

The fundamental difficulty in comparing fingerprint patterns is that no two images of the same finger are exactly alike, because friction ridge skin is flexible and stretchy. Never can you simply overlay two separate images and find that they perfectly align. If fingers were inflexible, static appendages, a science of individualization would be easier.

Comparison of two fingerprint images requires that each print be described as an arrangement of features-in-place, in which each feature is spatially related to every other feature. Because only a small number of distinct features have been discovered that apply to the patterns on fingers and in images of fingers, the features themselves are not sufficiently numerous to differentiate one pattern from all other patterns. When each feature is tied to a particular spatial location on the image, so each becomes a feature-in-place, then even a small number of different but reoccurring features can be arranged in an infinite number of spatial combinations. The method must include an objective procedure for a fingerprint examiner to construct this map of features-in-place. We describe current procedures in Chapter 3.

4. Objective standards for conclusions

The standards used to reach decisions in a scientific method are also quantitative. For example, a doctor decides whether to use medication for high blood pressure based on data of systolic and diastolic rates. Optimal pressure is less than 120 and less than 80, respectively. Normal blood pressure is 120-129/80-84, in which case the doctor checks regularly for change but does not medicate; borderline is 130-139/85-89, in which range the doctor includes other factors such as age, medical history, and family history in his decision; high blood pressure is defined as 140+/90+, and the doctor prescribes medication.

The doctor's decision to medicate when blood pressure exceeds 140/90 is based on a research literature that shows people above this range are at high risk for stroke, compared with people with lower pressures. The standard is assumed to be reliable, in that different technicians, measuring the same patient's blood pressure, would report similar ranges, and different doctors, observing the same ranges, make comparable decisions.

When a fingerprint examiner decides two fingerprints were made by the same finger, what standard does he use to decide? How much similarity must the two prints have? How can similarity be quantified? What standard permits an examiner to decide that the two prints differ sufficiently that two different fingers must have made them? How much difference must there be? How can difference be quantified?

The United Kingdom formerly had an apparently quantitative standard for fingerprint identifications. If the examiner found a single difference between a latent and exemplar that he could not explain, he excluded the exemplar; if fewer than 8 features corresponded in type and location between the latent and exemplar, the finding was inconclusive; if 8-15 features corresponded, he advised investigators of a likely match, but could not attest to an identification in court; if 16 or more, he made the identification and would so attest in court.

Unlike the doctor's decision, which is based on results of a wide body of research, there is *no* research evidence to show how many corresponding features are needed to assure an identification. The probability that 16 or more features in agreement means the same finger made both prints is untested and unknown. Also unlike the doctor's standard for prescribing medication, the fingerprint "measuring instrument" is unreliable, in that examiners disagree as to which features-in-place are in correspondence between two prints. We discuss the evidence for this claim in Chapter 8.

5. Objective definition of latent difficulty

Suppose you once again are searching for your wife in a large crowd. Suddenly, the lights go out. Visual features become useless. Your helpful host produces a few flashlights and candles. At what point is there enough visual information for you to uniquely identify your wife?

Latent prints, like faces in dim candlelight, rarely contain all of the information in the target. Most of the time, latents lack detail and clarity.

At present, there is no measure of the quality of a latent, either of how much information is present (how many features in their specified locations) or how clear that information is. Absent this measure, no empirical study can be performed to show how much detail or clarity is needed to individualize a latent.

6. Protection from bias

A scientific method defines procedures designed to prevent bias. For example, in collecting reports from witnesses to a crime, the police attempt to keep witnesses apart, so one witness cannot influence another. If a doctor needs to know a patient's white cell count, he must be assured that the blood sample was not mixed with other samples. In scientific experiments, enormous care is taken to prevent the experimenter (who is equivalent to the fingerprint examiner) from knowing the expected outcome of the test he is performing. Bias produces a higher number of erroneous outcomes (see Chapter 9).

Examples of fingerprint examiner exposure to bias include information, such as that the crime was a murder, or that there is other evidence connecting the suspect to the crime. In many crime laboratories, police investigators work side by side with fingerprint examiners. Many examiners are former policemen, still working in the same department, now with a different job. Biasing information is freely shared.

Another serious bias for a fingerprint examiner is exposure to the exemplar before he has fully analyzed the characteristics and features in the latent. We discuss biasing factors and their negative consequences in Chapter 9.

7. Training and proficiency testing programs

When each step of a method has been objectively described, that description can be translated into a training program that addresses each step. The objective description permits examiners in different places to receive comparable training, so that they apply the method in the same way. An examiner in Florida, trained in the method, reaches the same conclusion about the same latent-exemplar pair as an examiner in California. In the absence of a training program anchored to an objectively described method, examiners are trained differently, and reach different conclusions.

When each step of a method has been described quantitatively, a trainee examiner can be tested on that step to see whether he has mastered it. Similarly, he can be tested at the end of training to see whether he applies the method correctly.

A proficiency test could also be used for a practicing examiner, to assess his skill level or to determine whether he now needs further training in some specific area.

An objective method, as discussed above, includes a quantitative measurement of the difficulty of each latent. This measurement enables the test manufacturer to make multiple tests that are similar in difficulty, and to scale the difficulty of items in a single test. When there is no objective measure of a latent, the results of a test cannot be used to assess the examiner's skill, nor can two tests be objectively compared to one another. We discuss the problems with existing proficiency tests in Chapter 7.

2.7 Specification of a Method versus an Application of a Method

A method is a sequenced set of operations to carry out a defined task. Two examples of methods are: steps to compare two fingerprints to determine whether they were made by the same finger, and procedures for hormonal measurement to determine whether a woman is pregnant. A method describes steps in sequence, and includes instructions how to perform them to complete the task.

A given fingerprint comparison is an application of the method, not the method itself. As an example of the distinction, suppose your doctor wants to test you for strep throat. A throat sample, equivalent to a latent print, is submitted to a chemical test, comparable to a fingerprint comparison. The accuracy of the answer (do you have a strep throat) is unknown, just as the true donor of a fingerprint is unknown in casework. The laboratory technician who performs the actual test of the sample from your throat follows a rigorously prescribed procedure, a method to assess the sample. The steps and their sequence must be precise, so that if the sample contains evidence of strep throat, the result will be constant each time the test is applied. If laboratory technicians apply the method inconsistently, different outcomes occur for the same sample.

Each time the technician performs an analysis of a sample, he applies the method. The method can be evaluated by conducting experimental validity tests for its overall accuracy in identifying the presence of strep. The technician can be evaluated for his proficiency in applying the method. The truth of a particular outcome of a test is unknown, just as Stella Lavie does not know whether her identification of Mr. Lightfingers was correct.

Chapter 3

Fingers and Toes

Fingerprint comparison texts, as well as examiners testifying in court, frequently combine or confuse characteristics of fingers with those of fingerprints, which are *images* of fingers. In this chapter, we describe how flesh-and-blood fingers, exemplars (carefully made images of fingers) and latent prints (adventitious touches) differ. Latents and fingers often share few similarities, even though a latent fingerprint is made by the touch of a finger.

3.1 Friction Ridge Skin on Fingers

The surface skin of human fingers and palms, and toes and soles of the feet contains alternating ridges and grooves called *friction ridge skin*. These ridges and grooves developed to permit greater friction in grasping and walking. Along the ridges, irregularly spaced pores occur which exude substances loosely called sweat. Oil on the skin combines with these substances, so that the ridges of friction ridge skin, when they touch a surface, often leave an image of themselves.

The majority of criminal cases in which friction ridge skin is used to individuate people involve the patterns on fingers, rather than palms or feet. This is because fingers, as compared to other body parts, are much more likely to touch surfaces. The principles and problems are claimed to be the same for all areas of friction ridge skin (Ashbaugh, 1999).

We predict that some of the differences between fingers and palms, and between toes and soles create differences in the specifics of the comparison process. For example, the average area of the surface of a palm is approximately 20 times the size of an average finger. It is unknown whether this increases or decreases the number of features needed in agreement to make an accurate identification. Further, palms are characterized by major (deep) and minor (shallow) creases (called lifelines in another field), whereas creases are not a major component of the friction ridge skin of fingers. Ashbaugh (1999) has shown that these creases can be used in the comparison process of palms, which introduces a dimension to friction ridge skin found on palms that is not typically important when comparing prints from fingers. As another example, the embryonic formation of palms differs from fingers (Babler, 1991), which might make a difference in the uniqueness assumptions for the friction ridge skin of palms.

3.2 Images of Friction Ridge Skin Patterns

A perpetrator does not leave a finger at the crime scene, and the fingerprint examiner never looks directly at anyone's fingers. Fingerprint evidence introduced in court is not about fingers, but about *images* of fingers, and therein lurk some monster problems.

In a fingerprint comparison, a latent print (often called the crime scene fingerprint or mark, or unknown print) is compared to an exemplar (which has a known source). Latent prints are typically left inadvertently, sometimes on lousy surfaces for capturing an image, and contain only part of the friction ridge pattern on the finger. Exemplar prints are carefully made images on ideal surfaces that include as much area and detail as possible.

A. Exemplar Fingerprints: Inked and Scanned, Rolled and Plain

Two techniques are used routinely to make high quality images of the patterns of ridges and grooves on fingers under controlled conditions: ink and scans. The resulting images have different characteristics, depending on the technique employed. In either case, the finger can be lightly pressed straight down—a plain print, or gently and evenly rolled from side to side—a rolled print. A rolled, inked fingerprint is made by a skilled technician who gently and evenly rolls each finger over a black ink pad, with just enough pressure that the ridges are coated, but no ink flows into the grooves. Then the technician gently and evenly rolls each inky finger over a white card, so that the ink on the ridges is transferred to the card, reproducing the pattern of just the ridges in black ink, leaving the grooves white. The card consists of special paper that does not allow the ink to bleed. A rolled inked fingerprint is considered the best and most accurately reproduced image of the patterns found on the finger, because, at present, inked prints produce the highest resolution, clearest image of the pattern of ridges and grooves.

When the inked finger is pressed straight down lightly, the image is called a plain inked impression. While obviously smaller, because it does not include images of the ridges on the sides of the finger, it achieves equal clarity and resolution, and has two advantages over rolled fingerprints. There is less overall distortion of the ridges and grooves resulting from the flexibility of the skin on the finger, and the plain impression fingerprint includes a minimally distorted record of the information-rich delta and core areas (defined below).

When all ten fingers are shown on the same fingerprint card, the image is called a tenprint. Figure 3.1 shows the rolled exemplars of the ten fingers, and the ten plain impressions of the same person.

Digitally scanned fingerprints are increasing in use. No ink is necessary: the finger is either rolled or pressed down onto the glass surface of the scanner. The scanner makes a digital transformation in which ridges are dark and the grooves light in the scanned fingerprint.

Scanned fingerprints are as good as the resolution of the scanner and its associated software, and presently are generally of lower quality than images obtained with ink. Rolled, plain, inked and scanned fingerprints are collectively called exemplar fingerprints.

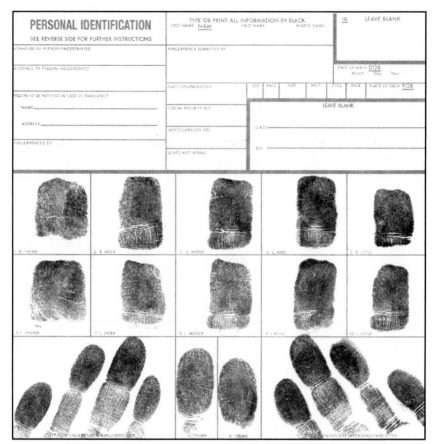

Figure 3.1 *rolled and plain impressions of all ten fingers: a tenprint.*

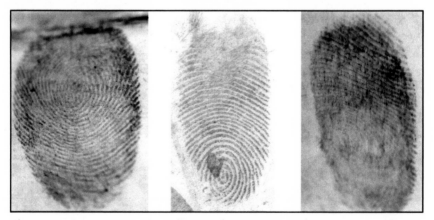

Figure 3.2 *Some examples of latent fingerprints left unintentionally.*

1. Differences between fingers and exemplar fingerprint images

The individual, true pattern of ridges and grooves occurs on the three-dimensional surface of a finger. Every two-dimensional image of that surface is a distortion of that baseline. For example, every photograph of a scene is a two-dimensional image of a three-dimensional space, and the distortion that results from that transformation is obvious from any single viewpoint of the scene. Similarly, a two-dimensional map distorts the shapes of every land mass as compared to its true shape reproduced on a three-dimensional globe.

The 3D to 2D transformation is only one of the many sources of the distortions present in every fingerprint. The flexibility of the finger's skin creates distortion of the friction ridge pattern every time the finger presses against a surface, so that a fingerprint neither fully nor identically reproduces the patterning of the ridges and grooves on the finger. No matter how expertly a rolled or plain exemplar is made, no two exemplars from the same finger will ever perfectly match. Figure 2.6 in the previous chapter illustrates four different (rolled inked) exemplars of the same finger. They do not look exactly alike.

Table 3.1 lists the different ways in which the patterning in exemplar images differs from those on the original finger.

Given these distortions, how many different fingerprints can Lyn Haber's left index finger make? Answer: an infinite number.

B. Latent Fingerprints

A latent fingerprint is an image of a finger left unintentionally, under uncontrolled conditions. Figure 3.2 shows some examples of typical latents.

1. Differences between fingers and latent fingerprint images

Latent prints differ from the actual patterns on the fingers in all the ways exemplar prints do, and add some major problems of their own. Most importantly, a latent image is usually further diminished in clarity and quantity. The additional differences between a latent image and the pattern on a finger are listed in Table 3.2.

We have characterized the differences between fingers and images of fingers, and how exemplar images and latent images are made. How are friction ridge patterns described? What features does a fingerprint examiner use to compare two patterns and determine, even though they do not line up exactly, whether they both came from the same finger?

Table 3.1
Differences Between Fingers and Exemplars of Fingers

- Transferring an image of a three-dimensional rounded surface of a finger to a flat two-dimensional surface of the print card causes substantial distortion.
- The friction ridge skin stretches and compresses under variations in the *amount* of pressure during the rolling or straight downward process.
- Each time the finger is rolled or pressed downward, the *direction* of pressure varies, which produces different distortions.
- Each time the finger is rolled or pressed downward, a different area of the finger touches the white card or the scanner, so the original pattern never appears exactly.
- The inking of the finger is different each time—too much ink may fill and obscure the grooves and insufficient ink may produce artificial discontinuities in ridges, both of which misrepresent the pattern on the finger.
- Scanning does not reproduce all the detail, due to poor resolution.
- Plain impressions show only part of the friction ridge skin surface.

3.3 Feature Description Systems

The fingerprint comparison method does not require a particular feature system, only that the descriptors be objective. We briefly review the two feature systems in widespread use today. The first is the Galton feature description, named after a nineteenth century fingerprinting pioneer; the second is the Ridges-in-Sequence system (RIS) developed by Ashbaugh (2005a) 100 years later.

Whichever system is used, evidence is needed of its reliability (the *agreement* among examiners in applying the system) and its validity (the *accuracy* with which the description determines whether two fingerprints were made by the same person or by two different people). In this chapter we discuss evidence of the reliability of the two systems of feature description. In Chapters 5 and 8 we present evidence of their validity.

3.4 Level 1 Ridge Flow Patterns

Both systems begin by classifying the overall ridge flow pattern over the entire print (called Level 1). The overall pattern of the flow of the ridges is the most noticeable characteristic of most fingerprints. The exemplars in Figure 3.3 illustrate some of the Level 1 patterns in general use.

Table 3.2
Differences Between Fingers and Latent Fingerprints of Fingers

- The size of an average latent print is only 1/5 of the size of the rolled print of the same finger.
- Excessive downward pressure of the finger on the surface obscures much of the pattern, light pressure fails to reproduce the pattern.
- Excessive lateral pressure of the finger on the surface produces distortion and smear in the pattern.
- Dirt on the surface obscures or alters the pattern.
- Over- and under-laid prints on the surface make separation of the target fingerprint more difficult, compared to looking at a single pattern on a single finger.
- Double taps create two partially overlapping prints of the same finger, and are often difficult to separate, compared to a single pattern on a single finger.
- Graining in wood or other patterns inherent to the surface mimic, distort or degrade the patterning on the finger.
- An irregular surface distorts the distances between ridges and grooves on the finger.
- The viscosity of the substance that produces the fingerprint distorts the patterning.
- The lifting process alters the patterning in the latent.

The direction of the flow across the finger is usually described in relation to two focal features: the *core*, defined as "the approximate center of the finger impression" (FBI Science of Fingerprints, 1984, Revised edition, p. 14) and the *delta* (often called a triradius), defined as the "area on the friction ridges where three ridge systems meet" (Ashbaugh, 1999, p. 225).

In the loop patterns (Figure 3.3, top row), the ridges flow in from one side of the fingerprint, up and over the core, returning under the core to flow out again from the same side from which they started. The top lefthand image in Figure 3.3 shows a right loop (the ridges flow in and then out from the right side). The top righthand image shows a left loop. In the whorl pattern (Figure 3.3, bottom left), the ridges flow in a circle around the core. Some whorls, like the one in Figure 3.3, have many circles, others have only one or two. In plain arch patterns, the ridges flow from one side to the other over the core, with no (1) angles of 90 degrees or less, (2) ridges that recurve and go out the same side from which they entered, or (3) upthrusting ridges that do not follow the general flow of the ridges (Cowger, 1993, p. 37). Arch patterns vary in vertical steepness of the ridge flow over the core, and in the degree to which the flow pattern appears vertical or slanted.

Level 1 patterns revolve around the core in different ways, so that finding the core and the pattern of flow around it help define the Level 1 pattern.

Deltas also help define the Level 1 classification. For example, a loop has only one delta, on the opposite side from the loop flow, whereas a whorl has two deltas, one on either side of the core and somewhat below the core (closer to the palm). Figure 3.4 reproduces Figure 3.3, with the Level I defining ridge paths highlighted. Cores are shown as small circles and deltas are drawn as squashed triangles.

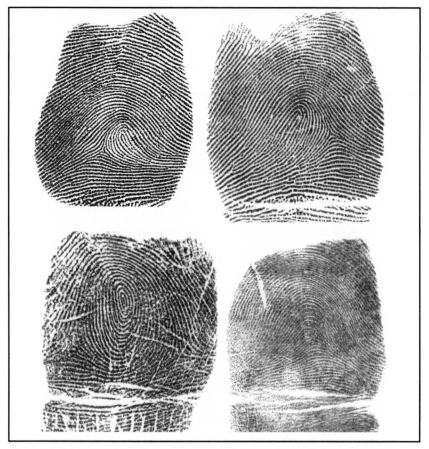

Figure 3.3 *Illustrations from exemplar fingerprints of the common level 1 patterns.*

Figure 3.4 *Schematic outline of the shape of the level 1 descriptors from Figure 3.3, with core and delta(s) indicated.*

Level 1 characteristics are usually—but not always—apparent in latent prints. If the latent print is small, it often is missing the core, or one or both deltas. The overall flow pattern may be difficult to determine if too much is missing. Distortions in the latent print may also obscure too much of the Level 1 pattern to label it unambiguously.

A. Uses of Level 1 Classification

Level 1 patterns provide a very quick way to divide prints into a small number of classes, although far too few to differentiate between individuals. They serve examiners in several important ways. One is to exclude a suspect as the perpetrator, without a time-consuming examination. If the crime scene latent fingerprint has a whorl pattern and the suspect's fingers all have loop patterns, the suspect could not have left that fingerprint.

Level 1 classification is often a powerful tool to orient the print. For example, in the whorl pattern, the deltas are located on either side, and towards the bottom, of the main whorl (see Figure 3.4, bottom left). If the deltas are visible, the core, which may not be included in the latent, must lie above them. Some latent prints with only a small amount of detail may still be oriented accurately from the Level 1 pattern.

B. Reliability of Level 1 Classification

Fingerprint examiners use differing kinds and names of Level 1 patterns (see FBI, 1984). Some examiners use only three (e.g., whorl, loop, arch); others divide these into subcategories (e.g., plain or tented arch, etc.). Also, some patterns, such as loops, vary on a continuum from very leftward sloping, to a bit leftward sloping, to a bit rightward sloping, to very rightward sloping. As with any continuum, division is arbitrary. For both reasons, individual examiners are expected to differ in their Level 1 classification.

There is no published research on the reliability of human examiners in specifying the Level 1 classification of latent fingerprints.

Beyond Level 1, both systems focus on smaller details, but the Galton and RIS systems diverge on which details are important. The Galton system uses a very small number of repeating characteristics on the ridge paths, and does not describe the paths themselves. The type of Galton feature, but not its exact location on the ridge, is the main concern. In contrast, the RIS system focuses on the paths of individual adjacent ridges, and the minutiae found on a ridge are anchored and ordered along that ridge.

3.5 Level 2: Galton Feature Descriptions

Unlike Level 1 characteristics, which occupy the entire print, Galton features are very small. Figure 3.5 shows the different minutiae characteristics in common use today.

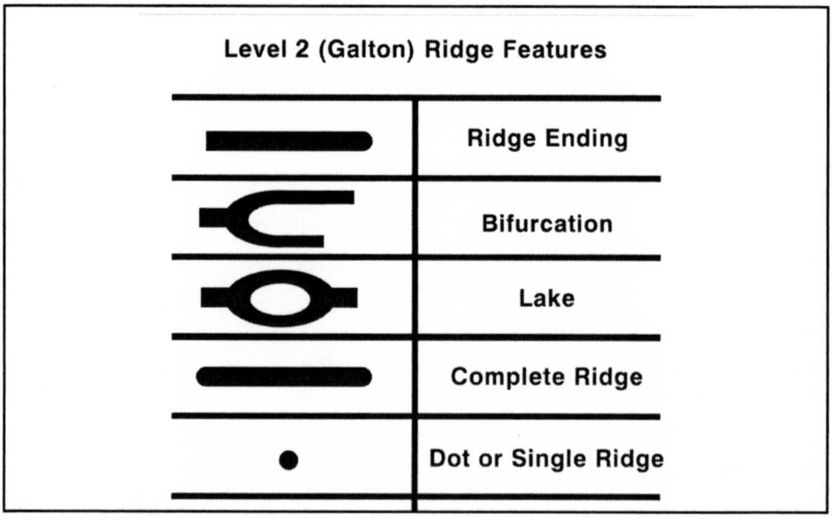

Figure 3.5 *Schematic Illustrations of some Galton minutiae.*

Figure 3.6 *An exemplar fingerprint, with some Galton minutiae indicated.*

The features shown in Figure 3.5 are called minutiae, or points, or Galton features. Figure 3.6 displays a small portion of an exemplar print in which several bifurcations and a ridge ending are circled.

According to the FBI, an average exemplar fingerprint contains 75 to more than 175 Level 2 features (the basis for this statement is unknown). In contrast, a low quality latent fingerprint may have only a few minutiae and many of those may be ambiguous as to their type (compare the feature details in the exemplars in Figure 3.3 with those in the latent prints shown in Figure 3.2).

A. Uses of Level 2 Galton Minutiae Descriptions

Level 2 features in their relative locations (described below) comprise the vast majority of the physical evidence in the fingerprint used by examiners to exclude and identify exemplars.

B. Reliability of Level 2 Galton Minutiae Descriptions

Several research studies have shown that highly skilled examiners *disagree* about the presence of a given feature (Evett and Williams, 1996; Langenburg, 2004; Langenburg et al., 2009). These experiments, discussed in detail in Chapter 8, suggest that the Galton feature description of a fingerprint is not reliable.

C. Defining Spatial Locations of Galton Features by Ridge Counts

A list of the Galton minutiae in a particular fingerprint is not sufficient to describe a fingerprint: lists are not patterns. To constitute a pattern, each minutia must be anchored in its location relative to each other feature in the fingerprint. Then the exemplar print is searched for the same features, in the same locations relative to each other. However, to be convincing that the features correspond between two prints, and are not in accidental agreement, the examiner must demonstrate that the entire constellation of Galton features appears in the same spatial position in both prints. Given the flexible nature of skin and other distortions, this is a challenging proposition.

Examiners use one of two spatial location systems: counting the number of *intervening ridges* between features or *eyeballing* the entire print. (Older systems, since abandoned, superimposed geometric grids of different kinds over the print. Olsen and Lee (2001) review these historical systems.)

Figure 3.7 shows a latent print with ridge count lines interconnecting five Level 2 features. The number of intervening ridges between each features are labeled.

Challenge. The difficulty with counting intervening ridges is that many of the factors that create distortion may also change ridge counts by obscuring a ridge or revealing a hidden (incipient) ridge. Then the intervening ridge counts between minutiae in the latent and its matching exemplar may not be the same. The amount of disagreement in ridge count permissible for a match now becomes subjective.

D. Reliability of Counting Intervening Ridges

The reliability with which examiners count intervening ridges between features in a latent print has never been studied. Nor has research tested examiner reliability in using ridge counts to establish which features are in spatial agreement in latent and exemplar pairs.

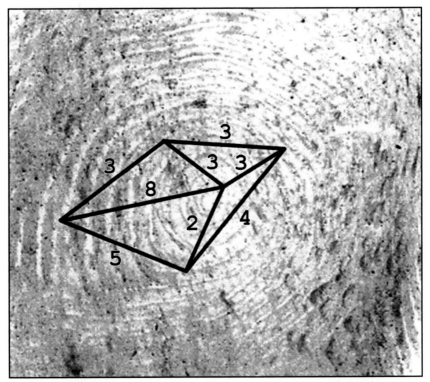

Figure 3.7 *Illustration of a latent print containing five indicated Galton features. For each pair of these features, the ridge count between the pair is drawn.*

E. Defining Spatial Location of Galton Minutiae by Eyeballing

Most examiners we have heard testify in court make subjective estimates of the spatial position of features. The examiner looks at some features in the latent and in the exemplar and judges that they are in the same spatial positions. This procedure is called *eyeballing*. Because the exemplar does not and cannot exactly overlap with the latent, the spatial positions of the relevant features never exactly match, so the examiner's decision accepts some amount of mismatch for each feature, a purely subjective decision.

F. Reliability of Eyeballing the Spatial Locations of Galton Features

No research has examined examiner reliability in reporting features in agreement by eyeballing their locations, but it seems obvious that the reliability of purely subjective eyeballing spatial locations is far lower than for the more objective procedure of counting intervening ridges.

Challenge

Without a known, acceptable reliability of a spatial location metric, examiner accuracy when assessing the amount of spatial agreement between different fingerprints is also unknown.

3.6 Level 2 Features in the Ridges-in-Sequence Description

The examiner who applies the RIS procedure selects an area in the latent print in which several adjacent ridges can be seen clearly enough to be followed. He starts with the beginning of the first ridge and lists each characteristic encountered in order, until the ridge ends. For example, in the latent print in Figure 3.8, the first ridge selected (toward the lower left hand corner) is part of the delta and very short. The next adjacent ridge (counting toward the core) starts to the right of the delta, goes up and then becomes indistinct. The third ridge starts to the right of the delta and soon ends, possibly adjoining the fourth ridge. The start of the fourth ridge is indistinct under the core; the ridge rises until it is adjacent to the second ridge, crosses right and over the core and becomes indistinct. The start of the fifth ridge is indistinct under the core; the ridge swings up and enters an indistinct area and then goes up and over the core and again becomes indistinct. The sixth ridge begins under the core, swings up and over the core and becomes indistinct as it begins downward again. The beginning of the seventh ridge is indistinct beneath the core; the ridge swings up and joins the eighth ridge to the upper left of the core. Ridges 4, 5, 6, 7 and 8 flow in parallel.

This analysis anchors each adjacent ridge to its beginning and its ending, as well as the relative location of every characteristic along each ridge. Measurements used for latent comparison are made up of complete ridges (both ends are visible), partial ridges (one end is visible), and internal (neither end is visible). Complete ridges, especially long ones, have more value in comparison, because more ridge events in sequence are involved. Ashbaugh claims that this description captures the ridge systems that make each print unique. This is a quantitative spatial position analysis, even though no linear measurement is made for the position of each feature along the ridge.

When the examiner follows the comparable ridges in the exemplar print of the same finger, he should encounter the same features in the same sequence.

Figure 3.8 *Illustration of a latent fingerprint on which Ashbaugh's ridges-in-sequence markings is highlighted.*

A. Reliability of Describing the Sequence of Features Along a Ridge

While no research evidence has demonstrated the reliability of examiners describing characteristics in order along a ridge, we would expect examiners to agree closely. This reliability still needs to be demonstrated.

Figure 3.9 *illustration of some Level 3 features observable in an exemplar fingerprint.*

3.7 Level 3 Description

The exemplar print shown in Figure 3.9 illustrates some very fine detail of the ridges themselves, including pore locations along ridges (these appear as irregular white circles in the ridges) and variation in ridge thickness. These are called Level 3 features. No count has been offered for the average number of Level 3 features in exemplars.

A. Uses of Level 3

The presence of Level 3 details has been labeled the most powerful tool to individualize (Ashbaugh, 1999), but these details are visible only in a very clear latent. Most examiners claim they do not use Level 3 features in making comparisons.

Challenge

Because Level 3 features are very small, their configurations are highly susceptible to variation in pressure. Ridge width, for example, varies each time a print is made, as does the distance between pores. Level 3 features may be untrustworthy as identification tools (Office of the Inspector General, 2006; Anthonioz et al., 2008).

B. Reliability of Level 3 Descriptions

Research on the stability of Level 3 details has not been reported, nor is there research evidence to show the amount of examiner agreement on the presence and type of Level 3 features.

Chapter 4

Where are the Fingerprints? Crime Scene and Laboratory Processing of Latent Fingerprints

Consider two crimes. In one, a masked, armed robber entered a convenience store at closing time through the front door and demanded money. The clerk handed him the contents of the register and told him the combination for the safe, which the robber tried to open. In the second case, a thief broke an apartment window, climbed through, and stole jewelry from a jewelry case in a dresser drawer.

4.1 Where are the Fingerprints?

Enter the crime scene investigator. Normally, latent prints abound: from the store clerks and customers in the first case, and from the tenant and her family in the second. Police and other officials also may leave their prints during their response to the crime call. The investigator who locates fingerprints at a crime scene makes a number of irreversible decisions. The most important choices are which surfaces to examine and which latent prints to keep.

The training and experience of the crime scene investigator who makes these decisions depend on the job description. In many crime laboratories, especially smaller ones, the job of crime scene investigator and fingerprint examiner are one and the same. In larger laboratories, the crime scene is investigated by someone who specializes in that job alone and may have relatively little or no experience with latent print examination.

A. Knowing Where to Look

Rarely can an investigator examine every possible surface. In the first robbery, the thief touched the knob of the safe. The investigator expects to find a thumb print on one side of the knob, with a print from the index and/or middle finger opposing it. Because the thief attempted to turn the knob, the prints are likely to include smear. In the second robbery, the investigator might predict two palm prints along the bottom sill of the window where the thief hoisted himself through. He expects those prints to exhibit extreme downward pressure. If he finds only one, he looks for additional prints from the other hand on the vertical window frame. He also examines the pull handles of the dresser drawer. He expects to find prints from at least the index and third finger on the underside of each handle, with a likely thumb print on the outside. If the thief picked up the jewelry case, the examiner expects a thumb print on one side, and most probably an index and/or middle finger on the other. In each of these instances, the presence of one print on an object directs the investigator's search for other prints. A skilled crime scene investigator predicts the location, the characteristics of the prints, and the specific fingers in the prints that he will find, given the perpetrator's intentions at that location.

B. Finding Invisible Latent Prints

The majority of latent fingerprints left at a crime scene are invisible to the naked eye. The perpetrator may have touched a surface such as cloth on which prints do not show. The crime scene investigator's task is to locate invisible as well as visible prints.

1. Enhancements to improve visibility

Menzel (2001) describes the special lighting and chemical procedures that are used at crime scenes to locate latent prints that cannot be seen with the naked eye. If a print is not suspected on a surface and is not visible, it is likely to be unnoticed and unused.

C. Lifting Visible Latent Prints

Visible latent prints are typically found on a smooth, hard surface, such as glass, tile, or glossy wood. These are normally lifted using powder. The investigator dusts the print lightly and evenly with powder, and places transparent sticky tape (sticky side down) over the surface on which the print is located so that the powder adheres to the tape. Then he lifts the tape up and smoothes it onto a white print card. The print is now visible on the card under the tape. This is a skilled task, and the quality of the transferred latent print varies with the choice of powder, amount of powder, the evenness and thickness with which the powder is spread over the latent print, steady and accurate positioning of the tape over the powdered latent print, uniformity of tension in removing the tape, and steadiness in placing the tape on the print card.

Most latent cards resemble ordinary white 3×5 file cards. They are pre-numbered by the investigator before arrival at the crime scene to aid in documenting the chain of custody (see below). On the reverse side of the print card, the investigator notes his name, the crime code, a sketch or description of the location of the print, and a record of the number(s) of each photograph taken of the latent print (see below). Occasionally, several nearby latent prints are lifted onto the same card.

4.2 Latent Print Value and Quality

If the crime scene investigator judges a print as too poor to use for comparison, he does not lift it. The crime scene investigator's written report documents the prints found, including the latent prints of no value and their locations.

Challenge

Because there is no metric for latent print quality, different investigators make different decisions about which latents to preserve.

Challenge

If the crime scene examiner has little training and experience in fingerprint comparison, he may make poor decisions as to which latent prints to retain for further examination.

Challenge

The research necessary to develop objective criteria for value has not been performed. Until the results are known, the profession cannot establish a quantitative standard for value. As we discuss in Chapter 5, there is also no research to show whether a poor print, discarded by the investigator as of no value for comparison, would still suffice to exclude a suspect, so that several value standards are necessary.

Challenge

What kind of training did the investigator receive that allows him to judge that a latent is of such poor quality it cannot be compared? Has he ever been tested on whether he discards useful latent prints?

4.3 Crime Scene Latent Print Documentation
A. Documentation of Chain of Custody

A well-documented record of the chain of custody routinely is required for all physical evidence, including latent fingerprints. Any break in the chain of custody creates the possibility of error: the evidence presented in court did not originate from the crime scene, or differs fundamentally from its original form. The chain is most frequently broken at the very beginning of a crime scene investigation, often in ways that are undocumented and even unnoticed (Fisher, 2003). For example, if the crime scene investigator worked several cases on the same day, the potential for inadvertently mixing up two cards is high. If a latent from an elimination subject lifted from one crime scene is accidentally included in the evidence from a different crime scene, the innocent person may become a suspect in the second crime. Only a complete chain of custody prevents this kind of confusion.

B. Photographic Documentation

Crime scene manuals (e.g., Fisher, 2003) describe a number of required procedures to document the location and surface on which each latent print was found. The most important is photographic evidence. This documentation prevents both careless mix-ups and fraud. Equally importantly, information about the orientation and location of the latent print and the characteristics of the surface helps the fingerprint examiner during analysis and comparison, as we discuss in the next chapter.

Normally, the crime scene investigator places a numbered label on the surface near the latent print, whether the print is visible or not. If a latent print is found on an object that will be removed from the crime scene, such as a knife handle, the investigator photographs the knife in place before it is moved, with appropriate tags visible.

In the rare instances when photographs cannot be taken, the crime scene investigator is required to make detailed drawings containing the same information on the back of the print card. Justification for failure to photograph is important, because drawings alone do not provide strong evidence that ties the latent(s) to the crime scene.

1. Digital photographic documentation

Many crime scene investigators now use digital cameras. Digital images can be altered with computer software such as Adobe Photoshop (Adobe Systems, Inc.), and, in extreme circumstances, digital pictures may be no better as evidence than freehand drawings. The crime scene investigator is required to describe that processing fully and to preserve the original disk from the digital camera so it is available for examination (Fisher, 2003). This anchors the latent to the crime scene. For traditional photographic images, the negatives serve this purpose.

C. Matrix Documentation

The crime scene investigator is in the best position to describe the matrix in which the print was made, such as sweat or blood.

Why does matrix information matter? Suppose the crime scene investigator notes in his report that he found latent print #3 on a banister, and the print was laid down in blood. A latent print examiner receives latent print #3, which has clear, thin ridge paths inconsistent with a blood matrix. A problem with the matrix can indicate a break in the chain of custody, or fraud.

D. Crime Scene Investigator's Bench Notes and Report

Collectively, the documentation of the evidence described above is contained in the contemporary bench notes and report written by the crime scene investigator. This report, signed and dated at the time of the work, should be included in the police report on the case. This report is essential to evaluate the completeness and accuracy of the crime scene investigation, to allow evaluation of the proficiency of the crime scene investigator, and to document that the investigation followed laboratory policy. The failure of the crime scene investigator to find an expected fingerprint, or the absence of a record of the investigator's attempt to find it, indicates a problem with the investigation: either in the training or skill of the investigator, or with its documentation.

Challenge

In our experience, it is rare that documentation of the crime scene investigation is introduced as evidence and even rarer for a crime scene investigator to testify in a fingerprint trial.

4.4 Crime Laboratory Processing of Latent Fingerprints

Most latent prints require some optical, mechanical or chemical enhancement to improve their visibility. A large number of techniques have been developed to enhance latent prints, depending upon the characteristics of the surface on which they occur and the matrix (such as blood or sweat) which produced the print (Lee and Gaensslen, 2001). Enhancement and processing techniques produce loss in the quality and quantity of the friction ridge pattern information to varying degrees. If more than one enhancement technique is applied, their sequence is a critical issue. Some techniques may destroy the print or the surface. Crime laboratory personnel are required to document the processing of the latent print in their reports, including photographs of the latent print taken before and after enhancement (Fisher, 2003).

Three characteristics of latent fingerprints frequently require further manipulation so they can be used to compare with exemplar fingerprints: (1) crime scene latent prints are always small; (2) there may be interference with the ridge patterns from details already on the surface; and (3) their visibility and contrast may not be adequate.

Latent prints are also manipulated to serve a specific purpose. If there is no suspect, the latent fingerprint can be processed and then submitted to an automated computer search to find a matching exemplar (see Chapter 6). As a different example, if the examiner decides to show the latent-exemplar pair to the jury, the prints are greatly enlarged, and markers are added that identify features in agreement.

A. Enlarging the Latent Print

An average latent fingerprint is often no more than a quarter inch across, roughly one-fifth of the size of a full plain fingerprint. Even with a high contrast ratio between the ridges and grooves, it is virtually impossible to follow a ridge path with an unaided eye.

Examiners routinely magnify prints for comparison purposes. These optical enlargements increase everything in the same proportion, so that if the size of the print is increased five times, then the width of each ridge and each groove is increased five times, as is the distance between them.

Enlargement creates penalties as well. The contrast between the ridges and grooves decreases, and every bit of visual noise, such as dust or dirt, is also enlarged.

B. Isolating the Latent

Three kinds of noise frequently interfere with the visibility of the friction ridge pattern in the latent. The target latent print is often laid down under or on top of another fingerprint from a different donor; the perpetrator may make multiple, overlapping touches on one surface; or the surface itself may possess a pattern that intrudes into the target print (wood grain is an example). In these cases, the examiner has to separate the target print from the noise.

Computer technology enables the examiner to display the original latent, noise included, on a computer screen. The examiner physically traces on the screen the path of each individual ridge in just the target print. The tracings of the target touch are retained in one file, and the remaining data in another. The examiner analyzes and compares the impression in the first file. Its fidelity depends on the accuracy with which the irrelevant details have been deleted without alteration of the target details.

Challenge
No research has been reported on the accuracy of reproduction of just a target latent from a composite of overlaid latent prints.

C. Alterations to Improve Image Quality
Computer programs, such as Adobe Photoshop, also have the capability to improve contrast to help differentiate grooves from ridges, to fill in gaps in ridge paths, and to remove noise such as dust particles, dense matrix or intrusions from the surface.

Challenge
In each alteration, the examiner makes a decision, based on his interpretation of the details in the latent. The resulting latent image differs from the original print, and may contain details that were not present in the original. There is no research to document the accuracy of these interpretations. However, a wide research literature has found that as more interpretation is needed, subjectivity and error increase.

D. Manipulation of Latent Prints for Automated Search Systems
In Chapter 6 we describe the use of automated search systems. At present, many of these systems require a human examiner to alter the latent before submission. Typically, the examiner manually traces major ridges and/or marks the location and types of features in the latent. The submitted image is now the human examiner's subjective interpretation of which ridge paths are important and their flow, and/or which features are present and their locations.

Challenge

No published research documents the kinds of errors that arise from different ways latents are prepared (see Chapter 6). More seriously, as we discuss in Chapter 9, if an AFIS search does not produce a candidate that appears to match the latent, the technician may reinterpret the latent and submit it a second time. This less likely interpretation increases the chances of an erroneous match.

E. Manipulation of Latent and Exemplar Prints to Show to the Jury

In many trials in which fingerprint comparison evidence is presented, the fingerprint examiner provides the jury with a display in which the crime scene latent and an exemplar print from the defendant are enlarged and shown side by side (see Federal Bureau of Investigation, 1988, Ch. 8).

To show the jury the similarity between the two prints, numbered markers on long lines are placed on the two enlargements that indicate the critical points of similarity, a display called a clock face.

These displays need to be drawn carefully, so that the ends of the lines do not obscure the features being indicated, and so that the lines themselves do not artificially enhance or reduce the appearance of similarity. When the lines and their numbers are in the identical arrangement over both images, the appearance of similarity between the two images is misleadingly enhanced, even though the critical features in the two images may not be in the same locations.

Challenge

No research has been reported to determine the extent to which clock-face displays assist the jury in understanding differences and similarity between fingerprints, including biasing decisions reached by a jury.

4.5 Crime Laboratory Documentation and Report

Because the processes carried out by crime laboratory personnel can alter the characteristics of the latent fingerprint, all aspects of laboratory processing must be described in a laboratory report, written by the appropriate laboratory technician.

Challenge

This kind of detailed report is rarely offered in evidence. Absence of this report is equivalent to a break in the chain of custody. The latent in its current form cannot be anchored back to the original print found at the crime scene.

Chapter 5

That's Your Fingerprint!
The ACE Comparison Method

Stella Lavie receives two fingerprints, a crime scene latent and an exemplar from a suspect. What method does she use to compare the prints? How does she decide whether the same finger made them?

The fingerprint profession asserts that forensic fingerprint comparison uses a science-based methodology (SWGFAST, 2002).

5.1 Introduction to the ACE Method

Fingerprint examiners today claim that they use an Analysis-Comparison-Evaluation method (ACE).

At each stage the examiner makes a binary decision based on a standard. In analysis, the examiner describes the physical evidence in the latent print and decides whether the latent contains enough quality and quantity of detail to use for comparison, applying a standard of *value*. During comparison, using the description of the latent, he looks for similarities and dissimilarities between the latent and suspect's exemplar. If all of the differences can be explained by distortions, he continues with the comparison. If not, he applies a standard of two-donor pattern dissimilarities to *exclude* the donor of the exemplar as the person who made the latent print. During evaluation, he judges the amount of agreement between the two prints against a sufficiency standard, and uses the standard either to *individuate* the suspect's finger as the source of the unknown latent print, or to conclude that there is *insufficient* agreement to either individuate or exclude the exemplar.

When the method is repeated by a different examiner using the same fingerprints, a last step is added, called Verification, and the ACE method may be called ACE-V, or ACE-ACE, depending on how the verification is carried out.

However, because ACE is a framework rather than a detailed method, as soon as the details are filled in (as we do here), most examiners will say that this version differs from the one they use.

A. How Many ACE Methods?

We know from examiner testimony offered in Daubert hearings and trials that individual examiners vary widely in their comparison practice. As one important example, Ashbaugh (1999) and the Office of the Inspector General of the Department of Justice (2006) assert that a complete analysis of the latent print must be performed before the examiner sees the exemplar, in order to prevent bias and backwards reasoning. In our experience many examiners begin analysis with the latent and exemplar side by side. The Office of the General Inspector (2006, p. 106) reports that several examiners they interviewed, including John Vanderkolk, a SWGFAST member and experienced examiner, describe analysis as an iterative, reversible and blending process in which the examiner's initial interpretation of the latent fingerprint may be adjusted during the comparison phase as it is informed by features seen in the known print.

The FBI's classic book, *The Science of Fingerprints* (1988), contains only a few pages on comparison procedures, but does not refer to that method as ACE and does not specify the steps of the method. Published versions of the method labeled as ACE differ, as discussed by Beeton (2001) and Triplett and Cooney (2006). Ashbaugh (1999) and Champod et al. (2004) have published the two most complete descriptions of ACE, and they do not completely agree.

Interpol (2005), the FBI (Stacey, 2004; Smrz et al., 2006; Budowle et al., 2006) and the Office of the Inspector General of the Department of Justice (2006) call for the publication of a detailed, official version of the ACE method. These organizations acknowledge the need for a fully described method with objective criteria that the profession applies uniformly.

Challenge

Published versions of the ACE method differ. Versions described by examiners differ. Exactly which procedures, then, comprise the ACE method? Cole (2007) argues that ACE is so ill-defined that it's wrong to call it a method.

B. Does the Fingerprint Profession Need a Specified Method?

Absolutely. Without a specified method, the method cannot be tested for its accuracy—the method would lack evidence of its *validity*. Without it, different examiners compare fingerprints differently, opening the possibility of different conclusions for the same latent-exemplar comparison—the method would be *unreliable*. Without sufficient specification, the method cannot support a *training curriculum*, nor can it be tied to *proficiency and certification testing*. These requirements are described in the Report of the National Academy of Sciences (National Academy of Sciences Report, 2009) and are listed in Table 5.1.

Table 5.1
Requirements for a Scientific Method to Compare Fingerprints. Taken from the National Academy of Sciences Report (2009, sections 6-6; 7-18; 8-16)

1. The method has a known validity. Validity is demonstrated by comparing the conclusions reached by application of the method with ground truth. When the method's validity is high, nearly all conclusions based on the method agree with ground truth.
2. The method is reliable. Reliability is shown by evidence that examiners reach the same conclusions when following the method.
3. The method is trainable. This is demonstrated by the success of a standardized training program.
4. The proficiency of examiners applying the method is demonstrated. Proficiency is shown by the results of a standardized proficiency testing program.

Challenge
The fingerprint profession has not adopted and endorsed a particular version of ACE. When an examiner attests he applied the ACE method, he cannot refer to a version approved by the profession: there is not one.

C. Our Overview of the ACE Method
We provide our own distillation of published descriptions by Ashbaugh (1999), Champod et al. (2004), P. Wertheim (2000), and our training in IAI-sponsored latent fingerprint courses, including ones taught by Ashbaugh (2005c) and K. Wertheim (2003). We present our description with sufficient detail to make each step of the method trainable and testable, so the progress of an examiner during training can be demonstrated, and the proficiency of trained examiners can be documented. We address the necessity for objective criteria for each conclusion an examiner makes. We include procedures to protect examiners from bias. As far as we know, the version of ACE described here is the most complete one to be published.

Table 5.2
Four Steps in the Analysis Stage of ACE

1. Judging the value of the latent print
2. Description of the physical characteristics of the latent
3. Selection of features in location
4. Setting confidence in problem areas

5.2 The Analysis Stage of ACE

The examiner's task in the analysis stage of the ACE method is to provide a complete, objective description of the physical evidence in the latent fingerprint, including the factors that support or diminish the trustworthiness of the pattern detail in the print.

The analysis Stage contains four distinct steps (Table 5.2). As a protection against bias and backward reasoning, the version of ACE presented here requires that these four steps be completed before the examiner sees the exemplar.

A. Analysis Step 1: Examiner Judgment Whether a Latent is of Value for Further Comparison

The value of a latent fingerprint rests on the quality and quantity of detail it contains, which in turn affect an examiner's ability to compare the latent to suspect exemplars. If a very poor quality latent is judged of value and then used for comparison, the conclusion is more likely to be in error. Also, the probability of an error on poor quality stimuli is even greater for people with lower levels of training or experience in the comparison process, or if the observers have been given biasing information (Dror et al., 2005).

Quality and quantity of detail represent an objective measure of the amount of information the print contains about the pattern of ridges and grooves. Assessment of value requires a physical measurement of the information in the latent print.

Table 5.3
Factors that Determine the Amount of Information in a Latent Print

1. Size (how much friction ridge skin is included in the latent)
2. Level 1 classification visible (e.g., whorl, loop, etc.)
3. Presence of focal features (core, delta)
4. Presence of orientation information (direction to tip of digit)
5. Amount of contrast between ridges and grooves
6. Local ridge quality (continuity); ease of following ridges
7. Amount of distortion (downward deposition pressure, lateral pressure)
8. Presence of surface noise (dirt, wood grain)
9. Surface regularity
10. Overlaid or underlaid prints
11. Smear
12. Number of Level 2 features visible (ridge length, bifurcation, ridge ending)
13. Level 3 features visible (ridge width, pores)

Table 5.3, drawn primarily from Ashbaugh (1999), is a sample list of the information components in a latent fingerprint. Each component can be measured in quantitative units.

Research can determine how to weight and combine these components into a single number that reflects overall quality and quantity of information.

Challenge
Results of such research have not been published.

Challenge
In the absence of the results of this research, the profession does not know which kinds of latents are most likely to lead to erroneous identifications.

When the measure of the quantity and quality of information contained in a latent is objective, an experiment could be used as a basis to set an objective standard for the value of a latent. In this experiment, 100 latent prints of varying levels of information content from 0 (no information at all) to 10 (the latent is as informative as the best rolled exemplar) are compared by examiners of varying levels of skill. Each of the 100 latent prints is paired with an exemplar. The majority of pairs are different donor, the rest same donor. The examiners are asked to carry out a full ACE comparison of each pair and conclude either identification or exclusion. No-value and inconclusive judgments are not allowed. The examiners are instructed to reach the most accurate conclusion they can, even for the least informative latent prints.

Figure 5.1 shows the hypothetical results from an experiment for the 100 latent-exemplar pairs averaged over all the examiners. Information content of the latents is shown on the horizontal axis ranging from 0 to 10. The percent of erroneous conclusions is shown on the vertical axis.

The results show that when the latent has no information, the probability of an erroneous conclusion is 0.50, equivalent to a pure guess. Fewer errors occur when the latents have better information content. The error rate approaches zero for the most informative latents.

Assume that the fingerprint profession decided that any latent that runs the risk of an error rate higher than 5 percent should be declared of no value. Using the hypothetical data in Figure 5.1, the value threshold should be set at 5, because latents of scores less than 5 lead to erroneous conclusions more than 5 percent of the time.

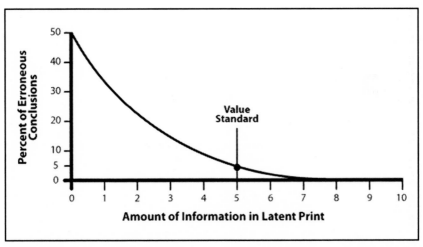

Figure 5.1 *Hypothetical results of examiners comparing latents of varying information to known exemplars. Information content of the latent is shown on the horizontal axis, and number of erroneous conclusions is shown on the vertical axis.*

Figure 5.2 displays the same hypothetical results, averaged over all examiners (as in Figure 5.1), but now the results from the same donor (solid line) and different donor (dotted line) pairs are separated.

The results show that single donor pairs require a more informative latent to restrict errors to the same 5 percent standard. A latent of level 6 is needed to identify the exemplar. The Figure also shows that a latent of level 4 can be used to exclude an exemplar.

Figure 5.3 combines same and different donor pairs (as in Figure 5.1), and shows the relationship between latent value and examiner skill. In this Figure, the latent print examiners (LPEs) are separated into two groups, high skill and much lower skill (determined by a good proficiency test). The results show, as would be expected, that the high skilled group (dotted line) makes fewer errors overall and is more accurate at each information level, compared to the low skilled group (solid line). If the same error rate standard is used (reject latents that produce more than 5 percent erroneous conclusions), the high skilled examiners can compare latents of content 4 or above, whereas the low skilled examiners need latents of 6 or above to avoid making more than 5 percent errors.

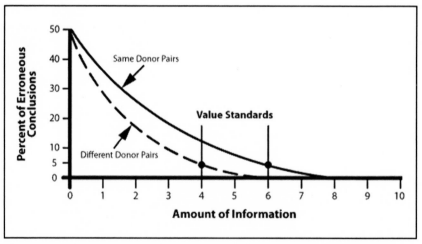

Figure 5.2 *The same hypothetical results for examiners, but with the results reported separately for pairs from the same donor (correct response is Identification) and for pairs from different donors (correct response is exclusion).*

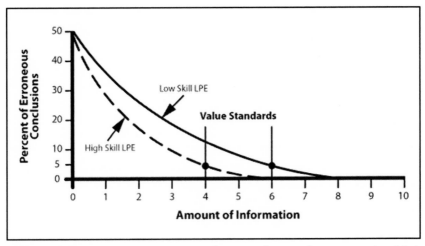

Figure 5.3 *The same data, now combining all pairs, but separating high and low skilled examiners.*

Challenge

This experiment has never been performed, and cannot be, until there's an objective measure of the amount and kind of information present in the latent. In the absence of the results from this experiment, the profession cannot know the probability of an erroneous conclusion.

1. A standard of latent print value

After the examiner assesses the information content of the latent print, he applies a value *standard* to the amount of information content found. As we described in Chapter 2, standards refer to arbitrary decision points along a scale of an objective measurement. For example, using the data in Figure 5.1, the profession might choose information content 5 as the threshold for value. Latent prints containing less than this amount of information would not be used for comparison, because the probability of an erroneous identification is too high. Latents of content 5 or more pass the *comparison value standard*, so the examiner would continue the examination.

The fingerprint profession could set more than one value standard. Using the hypothetical results in Figure 5.2, the profession might stipulate that all latents of content 3 or less be discarded, but level 4 latents could meet an *exclusion value standard*, in which a latent print could be used to exclude an exemplar, but should not be used for other comparisons. For example, a very low quality latent might contain enough detail to identify it as a whorl. If the suspect did not possess a single whorl, that suspect could be excluded.

As a different kind of example, examiners generally agree that AFIS algorithms require higher quality latents to conduct a useful search. At present, the higher quality judgment is subjective, and is up to the individual examiner. The profession could set a separate value standard for submission to AFIS. This standard would depend upon research that shows the relation between the difficulty of the latent and the probability the system will produce highly ranked candidates known to be erroneous.

Challenge

The fingerprint profession has not set a value standard. Each value judgment is made subjectively by the individual examiner.

2. Reliability of value conclusions

Given the absence of an objective measure of difficulty and of a standard established by the profession, examiners are likely to differ in their judgments about the value of a given latent print. The evidence shows they do. For example, some proficiency tests from ASCLD and CTS included a few latents of greater than usual difficulty and asked examiners to conclude value or no-value for them. Those results showed examiner variance on judgments of value (Peterson and Markham, 1995). In experimental data, R. Smith (2004) presented examiners in a single crime laboratory with latents judged by experts to be of value. The examiners rejected nearly half of the prints as of no value for comparison (described in detail in Chapter 8).

These examples show that the value standard is unreliable (different examiners reach different decisions about the same print) and invalid (the criteria for value have not been established in a way that can be measured and tested).

B. Analysis Step 2: Description of Physical Characteristics of the Latent

In this step, the examiner identifies the physical evidence visible in the latent and records every factor that would cause this particular latent to differ from an exemplar from the same donor. These factors, adopted and expanded from Ashbaugh (1999), are shown in Table 5.4.

These characteristics describe the causes and ways in which this particular latent is a distorted representation of the friction ridge system of an exemplar from the same finger. Distortions are created when the print is laid down, lifted and/or processed. By listing these distortions in the latent, all differences between this latent and an exemplar of the same finger are predicted ahead, *before the examiner sees the exemplar*. We describe each of these nine factors briefly.

Table 5.4
Factors that Create Differences Between a
Latent and Exemplar of the Same Finger

1. Substrate Factors
   a. Flexible surfaces, such as plastic bags
   b. Discontinuities in the surface
   c. Irregular shape
   d. Uneven surface
   e. Dirt, water
   f. Soft surface
   g. Overlaid/underlaid prints
   h. Noise
2. Matrix Factors
   a. Sweat/Sebaceous oils
   b. Wet
   c. Mud-type
   d. Heavy viscosity
   e. Corrosive
3. Development Medium Factors
   a. Powders
   b. Ninhydrin
   c. Iodine Fumes
   d. Cyanoacrylate
4. Enlargement and Enhancement Factors (see Chapter 4)
   a. Magnification
   b. Contrast enhancement
   c. Photoshop manipulations
5. Downward Deposition Pressure
   a. Amount
   b. Consistency with alleged method of leaving the fingerprint
6. Lateral Deposition Pressure
   a. Smear
   b. Double taps
   c. Consistency with alleged method of leaving fingerprint

continued…

Table 5.4 (continued)

7. Anatomical Aspects
   a. The nature or purpose of the touch
   b. Orientation of the print
   c. Source of print (finger, fingertip, palm, sole etc.)
   d. Likely digit source (thumb, little finger etc.)
   e. Consistency of digit with alleged purpose of touch
8. Physical Evidence Visible in the Print
   a. Raindrops, etc.
   b. Amount of force and its direction in the print
   c. Smear or double tap due to function of touch
9. Problem Areas
   a. Abrupt changes in matrix
   b. Apparent different development media
   c. Misaligned ridges

Figure 5.4 *Examples of latents deposited on surfaces of different textures.*

1. Substrate factors

The fingerprint is altered by characteristics of the surface on which it is deposited. Figure 5.4 shows three latent prints deposited on three different surfaces. The latent to the left in the Figure is made on rumpled plastic, the center shows a latent on clean, flat glass, and to the right the latent is deposited on wood.

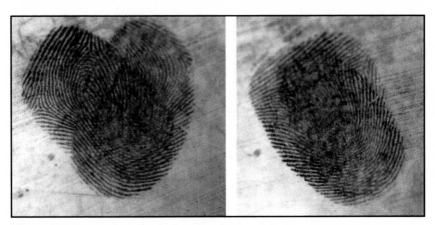

Figure 5.5 *Examples of overlapping latent prints.*

Patterning in the surface, such as wood grain, can sometimes be difficult to differentiate from patterns of ridges and grooves. When such latents occur, the examiner explains in his bench notes the method used to make this distinction.

When more than one fingerprint is found on a surface, such as a teller's counter, and the prints overlap, the examiner's task is to identify the overlap and separate the latents. His bench notes describe what led him to identify overlapping prints and the justification for the specific separation he made. Figure 5.5 gives two examples of overlapping prints: a "zipper" appearance of two prints laid down at different angles to one another on the left, and continuous ridges from different prints on the right.

Discontinuities in a latent often arise from discontinuities in the surface on which the print was deposited. If the print is laid down on a folded piece of paper, unfolding the surface produces a discontinuity in the ridge paths. Plastic bags, which tend to rumple, frequently result in discontinuities that cannot be aligned across the break. The examiner notes the discontinuity in his bench notes. When the ridges cannot be exactly aligned, features from these two areas of the print cannot be combined to use for comparison, because their spatial relations are unknowable.

2. Matrix factors

Matrix refers to the substance that transferred the patterns of the ridges and grooves of the finger onto the surface. The fingerprint pattern is altered by the matrix. Typically, the matrix is a combination of internally generated material (sweat, sebaceous oils from other body parts) and external material, such as ink, blood, motor oil, etc. Viscous fluids, such as motor oil, widen and blur the appearance of the ridges. Figure 5.6 gives an example of a latent made in oil (left side of Figure 5.6) and one created by sweat (right side of Figure 5.6).

The examiner who notes that the latent was laid down in oil *expects* to see thinner ridges in the exemplar; and *expects* that ridge width, blurred in the latent, will not reflect significant width differences apparent in the exemplar. Having made this observation, the examiner cannot use a readily visible thickening of a ridge in the latent as a useful feature for comparison, even if it were to occur in the exemplar.

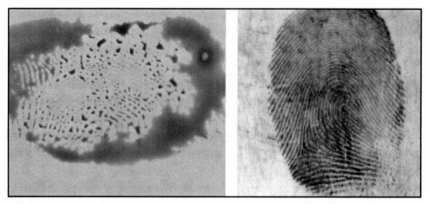

Figure 5.6 *Examples of different matrices, a latent deposited in oil and another in sweat.*

3. Development medium factors

The fingerprint is altered by the method used to develop it. Specific development processes have associated characteristics, which Ashbaugh (1999) refers to as *signatures*. For example, excessive ink can fill in grooves, obscuring ridge detail; powder can fill in ridge endings, creating an apparent continuous ridge. Ninhydrin (used extensively to make prints visible that were laid down on paper) can create apparent breaks in the ridge path where the ridge is continuous. In the most extreme cases, the development process may destroy the fingerprint altogether. The examiner's bench notes include the type of development process used.

4. Enlargement and enhancement factors

Because latent prints are typically only a few centimeters in size and frequently of poor contrast, examiners routinely use techniques to improve the print's visibility. A five-power magnifying glass or computer-produced enlargement is standard equipment. Extreme enlargement may make features visible at the expense of breaking up continuous ridge paths. Manipulations in Photoshop and comparable programs, such as highlighting ridges or features in color, or adding contrast, potentially alter the print. We described these techniques and their hazards in Chapter 4.

5. Downward deposition pressure

The fingerprint is altered by the amount of downward pressure exerted when the print is deposited. Figure 5.7 shows two takes of the same finger, in which downward deposition pressure is varied.

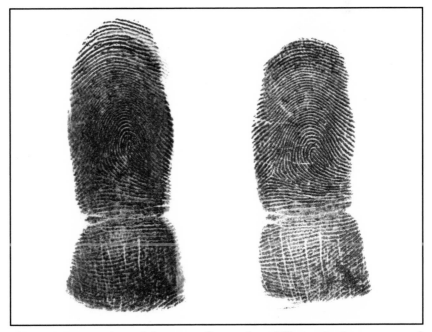

Figure 5.7 Two takes of the same finger that different in the amount of downward pressure.

According to Ashbaugh (1999), in the lightest deposition pressure, it's hard to see much detail. A print made with medium deposition pressure contains the greatest detail and clarity. (Medium downward pressure is desired when a police officer makes a plain, straight-down exemplar print.) Heavy deposition pressure fills in or alters fine detail, especially third level detail. Extreme deposition pressure obscures all detail in the center. Notice what happens to the ridges and grooves as a result of deposition pressure. Heavy pressure (shown to the left in Figure 5.7) flattens the friction ridges so the grooves are very narrow or even obscured, compared with medium pressure (shown to the right in Figure 5.7), in which the ridges are not as wide and the grooves are more visible.

6. Lateral deposition pressure

The appearance of ridges and grooves is altered by lateral (sideways) pressure. When a police officer makes a rolled print, the finger's skin is pushed to the side in the direction of the roll. A carefully made rolled print flattens and expands, then squishes the ridges laterally. In contrast, a straight-down print flattens and expands the ridges in the center of the image. These "squished" changes in the ridges have never been described fully, yet they are entirely predictable.

When you pick up a regularly curved surface, such as a can (without tilting it to drink from it), you create this kind of sideways pressure on your fingers (in contrast to straight downward pressure). Figure 5.8 illustrates a lateral distortion when touching a hard rounded surface.

7. Anatomical aspects

These refer to which finger was used, and for what purpose. The nature or purpose of the touch by the finger alters the characteristics of the fingerprint.

The latent digit(s) and their orientation must be consistent with the supposed purpose of the touch. Suppose a policewoman states that she stopped a man riding a bicycle at night without a light, and the man grabbed her flashlight by its head and beat her with it. On the flashlight is found only one usable latent print, which is identified as the defendant's right thumb. The defendant, who claims the policewoman beat him unconscious, says he has no memory of ever touching the flashlight. Assume the match is correct. The question is whether the latent and its orientation are consistent with the policewoman's version of what happened, or with the defendant's. Figure 5.9 illustrates the scenario described by the policewoman. The suspect holds the flashlight to swing it as a weapon, and the assumed position of an assailant's fingers on the flashlight can be seen. Notice the downward orientation of the thumb. However, Figure 5.10 shows the actual location and orientation of the suspect's thumbprint. It is inconsistent with the policewoman's version of how the flashlight was held as a weapon (the thumb is in the wrong orientation), suggesting that her testimony is wrong.

Figure 5.8 *An example of touching a spherical surface, producing lateral distortion.*

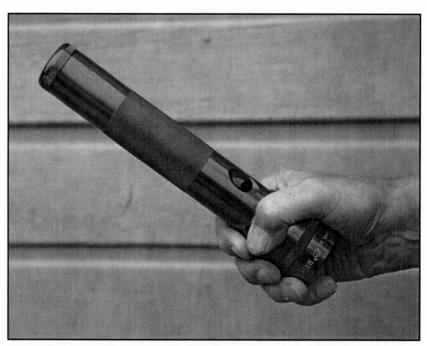

Figure 5.9 *An illustration of a description from a police officer of how an assailant held a heavy flashlight to hit her on the head.*

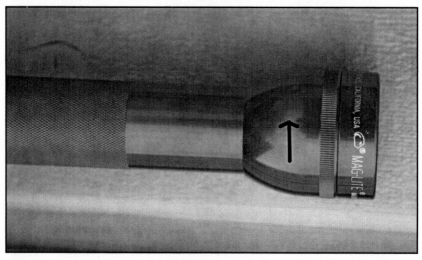

Figure 5.10 *The location and orientation of the assailant's right thumb print on the flashlight is indicated by an arrow, with the tip of the arrow pointing toward the thumb's tip.*

Notation of these characteristics can bolster a case, or be used to support a claim that the latent has been mislabeled or fraudulently constructed. As another example, suppose a robbery occurred on a rainy night, during which the perpetrator allegedly left a latent on the windowpane he broke when entering the house. The fingerprint examiner sees water drops in the latent lifted from the pane, and identifies the print to Mr. Mo. Mr. Mo will have some difficulty explaining he left that latent innocently on a different occasion. As a different example, suppose a fraud case in which the print is alleged to have been lifted from a cardboard box containing checks. The box has disappeared (which seems to happen inexplicably and deplorably frequently), and the fingerprint examiner notes that the substrate from which the latent has been lifted is consistent with a flexible surface. This suggests a mismatch between the original print and the one now in evidence.

8. Problem areas in the latent

Ashbaugh (1999) warns the examiner to avoid analyzing individual ridge paths or features in areas in a latent if they are of such poor quality that they cannot be used for comparison, or to treat the information found in them as highly uncertain. These areas are flagged in the bench notes.

9. Worksheets and bench notes

Ashbaugh (1999) recommends that the entire analysis of the physical evidence be recorded contemporaneously on a worksheet that becomes part of the report. Table 5.5 illustrates a worksheet modeled on one Ashbaugh (2005b) developed for Canadian examiners.

The most important point about distortions is that they rarely affect a single ridge. In general, the description of a distortion in the latent predicts differences in areas of adjacent ridges. The description in the latent of larger areas expected to differ from the exemplar, in specific ways, is a scientific power that has been untapped, untested, and unevaluated by the fingerprint profession.

Challenge

The factors that create distortion have never been either fully specified or subjected to testing. There is no research to show whether examiners can classify different changes in ridge path and shape according to the source of distortion (e.g., shape of the substrate surface vs. deposition pressure). There is no research to show whether examiners can predict what a relatively undistorted exemplar print would look like, given a distorted latent. Knowledge of distortion is essential in the subsequent comparison stage, to distinguish between differences caused by distortion and those caused by two donors.

Table 5.5
Bench Note Form for Analysis Stage of ACE (from Ashbaugh, 2005)

Space for date, crime lab, examiner, case number, suspect name/
number, and latent print number are deleted, as well as space for the
examiner's responses.

Clarity rating:
    Quality of observable detail of the friction ridges.
    Clarity rating dictates the level of tolerance for discrepancies.
    1st level detail—is the overall friction ridge pattern observable?
    2nd level detail—quantity and quality of observable major ridge
        formation?
    3rd level detail—observable intrinsic ridge and pore formation?

Substrate Distortion:
    Material upon which the matrix is deposited may cause distortion
        (e.g., creases in plastic).
    Can the substrate material be determined?
    What is the condition of the substrate (e.g., dirty, soft, shape,
        flexible)?

Medium Distortion:
    Medium is the substance deposited by the friction ridges (e.g., sweat
        contaminated with oil and dirt).
    Are the characteristics of a wet print observed?

Development Matrix
    Each development matrix (e.g., chemical reagent) reacts with a
        specific material(s) known to be present in the latent fingerprint
        residue.
    Reaction results in a change in appearance (e.g., color).
    What is the appearance of the developed friction ridge impression
        (e.g. black powder; ninhydrin, cyanoacrylate)?

Pressure Distortion
    Relates to distortion created by pressure exerted by the individual's
        hand or digit on the substrate.

continued...

Table 5.5 (continued)

Downward pressure or vertical weight being placed on friction ridges (generally changes the friction ridge shape: flattening or broadening each ridge).

Lateral or horizontal pressure distortion (usually accompanied by sideways sliding of the friction ridges and smearing).

Flexibility of friction ridge skin taken into account?

Skin cannot be distorted in more than one direction at once: if so, two prints involved rather than one.

Red Flags

Any indicators of 'red flags' present (e.g., ridge disturbances, sudden differences in appearance of matrix or medium lines through the pattern area, misaligned ridges, extra thick ridges, hatch ridges, crossovers, angular joints, similar shaped major ridge path deviations in close proximity, substrate artifacts, lack of harmony in distortions, matrix smears double taps)?

Ridge Path Configuration

Establish the route of each ridge path (e.g., run the ridges and grooves).

Independent ridge paths should be discernible, their flow should be in concert.

Intrinsic Ridge Formations

Third level detail

    e.g., ridge shape, thickness

    e.g., pore size, shape and position

Anatomical Factors

Digit determination: what part of the palmar or plantar surface.

Is information available of the physical spatial aspects (e.g., where the print was located on the substrate)?

Can any time frame of likely deposition be established based on location (e.g., after glass was broken)?

Challenge

There is no requirement that examiners document and record the latent print's distortions in their bench notes, or include them in their laboratory report. In this country, examiners rarely record bench notes of their analysis. The absence of these contemporaneous notes opens the examiner to backwards reasoning, in which he "sees" characteristics in the latent based on the exemplar.

C. Analysis Step 3: Selection of Friction Ridge Features to be Used for Comparison

In the third step in the analysis stage, the examiner labels and locates the friction ridge characteristics that are reliable to use in the subsequent comparison stage.

1. Minutiae feature description

In Chapter 3, we described and illustrated Galton minutiae and the two methods in use to locate them: eyeballing and counting the number of intervening ridges between pairs of features.

Challenge

Research findings indicate that examiners analyzing the same latent print disagree whether Galton features are present. For example, Langenburg (2004) asked examiners to look at a series of single latent fingerprints, and for each one, count the ridge endings and bifurcations they found (the data are reported in detail in Chapter 8). Skilled examiners disagreed with one another about which features were present. A comparable result was reported by Evett and Williams (1996), also discussed in Chapter 8.

Does it matter that examiners disagree as to which features are present? Yes! The ACE method of fingerprint comparison cannot be reliable and valid if experts disagree about the presence of the very features they use to compare.

2. Ridges-in-sequence feature description

In Chapter 3, we described and illustrated Ashbaugh's ridges-in-sequence system, which uses ridge length and the order of features along each ridge path in sequence as the basic metric.

Challenge

Experimental evidence is needed to show examiner accuracy and reliability in identifying features using ridges in sequence.

Challenge

Experimental evidence is needed to demonstrate examiner accuracy in specifying the spatial position of individual features. The two spatial methods, eyeballing and counting intervening ridges for minutiae, need to be compared for their accuracy, and the winner compared with locating features using ridges in sequence.

Challenge

While no research has evaluated "visual eyeballing" to map spatial location, research in visual perception shows this method to be error prone, invalid, and unreliable (Haber and Hershenson, 1980).

3. How many minutiae or adjacent ridges should be selected in the latent?

Examiners disagree as to how many features in the latent need to be pre-selected during analysis. Some examiners argue that every usable feature in a latent must be labeled and located before the exemplar is viewed. Others use what they consider to be a sufficient number of features, and then quit. Similarly, the number of adjacent ridges needed has not been specified.

Challenge

ACE does not specify this component. The answer could be established by research that would relate the quantified information content of the latent to the number of features-in-location needed for correct conclusions.

D. Analysis Step 4: Documentation of Confidence in Different Areas of the Latent

In Step 2 of analysis the examiner notes areas of poor value to avoid during comparison. What confidence can he place in features observed in the remaining areas?

Ashbaugh (1999) refers to this analysis step as *setting tolerances*. Suppose the latent includes a crisp, undistorted core in which many features are visible. The examiner would place high confidence in those details. If any of them failed to appear in the exemplar in the same relative locations, the examiner can exclude the exemplar with assurance. Now take a more typical example, in which areas of the latent that the examiner plans to use for comparison are distorted. Extreme lateral pressure might obscure a ridge. Very light downward pressure might cause an artificial ridge break. In the first case, the examiner should note a possible range of number of ridges within the specified area. In the second, the examiner should note that this specific feature looks like a ridge ending, but might be a continuous ridge; he does not know which. He makes his best guess, and attaches a low confidence level to that guess.

Ashbaugh (1999) argues that an examiner must depend on these tolerance levels during comparison. The greater the confidence assigned, the lower the tolerance for any mismatch found later. Establishing confidence levels for different parts of the latent prevents the examiner from changing his decision later based on information in the exemplar.

Challenge
We have not observed many examiners setting confidence limits during analysis. In the absence of this step, they are open to backward reasoning once comparison begins.

5.3 The Comparison Stage of ACE
The examiner's task in the comparison stage is to describe and account for the differences between the latent and the exemplar.

The comparison stage of ACE consists of five steps, described in Table 5.6.

Table 5.6
Five Steps of Comparison Stage

• Description of Distortion in Exemplar
• Specification of Sets of Features in Their Locations
• Predictable vs. Inexplicable Differences
• The Exclusion Standard
• Counting Features in Agreement in Type and Location

A. Comparison Step 1: Description of Distortions in the Exemplar
Whether the suspect's exemplar has been inked or scanned, rolled laterally across a surface or pressed straight downward, predictable distortions arise that create differences between the exemplar and the latent. The examiner notes those distortions in the exemplar.

B. Comparison Step 2: Marking Sets of Features or Ridges in Their Corresponding Spatial Locations
The examiner begins with a subset of the features/ridges he had selected in the latent print during analysis, and looks for them in the corresponding locations in the exemplar.

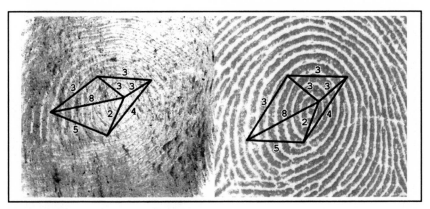

Figure 5.11 *A latent and exemplar print showing corresponding locations of five minutiae indicated by ridge count lines connecting them and the number of ridges between each feature.*

Using features as minutiae, Figure 5.11 shows a latent and exemplar from the same donor with 5 roughly corresponding features. In this figure, correspondence of location was determined by counting intervening ridges between the pairs of features. If the examiner finds that all of the features agree by type and location, he repeats this process for the rest of the features labeled during analysis, always comparing from latent to exemplar.

Challenge

Unreliability in locating features in relation to each other can occur when distortion creates mismatches in ridge counts. When and how much disparity in count can be accepted is presently a subjective decision made by the individual examiner.

If the examiner uses a ridges-in-sequence procedure for spatial location, he begins with the first ridge he had selected in the latent and follows it as far as he can in the exemplar, comparing the ridge flow and ridge events along the ridge path to those he had noted in the latent. If they agree in distance and kind, he repeats the comparison with an adjacent ridge, etc. Figure 5.12 illustrates the results of this process using a matching latent-exemplar pair.

Figure 5.12 A latent and exemplar print showing corresponding ridges in sequence.

Challenge

The specification of corresponding spatial position across two prints can be no better than the spatial position measurement in the latent fingerprint itself. As we observed in Chapter 3, examiners often depend on subjective eyeball judgments. When comparison begins, those examiners again make subjective eyeball judgments. There is no evidence of the accuracy of perceptual judgments of spatial location similarity, and none about its reliability. We expect the reliability to be very poor.

When does the examiner stop comparison? K. Wertheim (2003) taught that the examiner ends comparison when he is certain he has found "enough" agreement. We return to the vexing question of enough in our discussion of evaluation.

Challenge

Examiners differ in the amount they compare, because the ACE method has failed to spell out the procedure for this step. The answer needs to be determined by research (described below) that shows how much agreement is needed to assure an accurate outcome, to a known probability.

Challenge

In practice, many examiners report that they compare the latent and exemplar side by side, looking back and forth between them. Every time an examiner first identifies a feature in the exemplar and then searches for it in the latent, he opens himself to bias and increases the probability of an erroneous identification. We discuss the intrusion of this kind of bias in Chapter 9.

C. Comparison Step 3: Distinguishing Between Distortions (Two Takes of the Same Finger) and Two-Donor Pattern Differences (Images from Two Different Fingers)

The uniqueness assumption asserts that the patterning of features will differ in two latents made by two different donors in ways that cannot be confused with the apparent differences that arise from distortions of a single pattern (see Chapter 2).

1. Specification of distortions and two-donor pattern differences

In the third step of comparison, the examiner notes every difference between the latent and exemplar. A *distortion* is consistent with a distortion in the latent print he had noted and labeled in his bench notes during analysis. A *two-donor pattern dissimilarity* cannot be accounted for by a distortion listed in those bench notes.

Challenge

Distortions have not been described quantitatively, and there is no evidence that examiners can label distortions correctly.

Challenge

There is no quantitative metric of the distinction between a distortion and a two-donor pattern dissimilarity. The Glossary published by SWGFAST (2003) offers the following: "DISCREPANCY a difference in two friction ridge impressions due to different sources of the impressions (exclusion). DISSIMILARITY see *Discrepancy*. DISTORTION variances in the reproduction of friction ridge skin caused by pressure, movement, force, contact surface, etc." This is a circular definition, not a metric for the difference. Despite the SWGFAST Glossary, the fingerprint profession does not have a consistent terminology for this distinction. In the fingerprint literature, the words "difference," "dissimilarity," "distortion," and "discrepancy" can refer to disagreement between two prints resulting from either one or two donors.

Challenge

Without bench notes, and prevention of bias, the distinction between distortion and two-donor pattern difference is open to backward reasoning. In Chapter 9 we show an example from a real case of the power of this bias to lead to an erroneous identification.

D. Comparison Step 4: The Exclusion Standard

The uniqueness principle requires that when a single two-donor pattern dissimilarity between a latent and exemplar is found, the examiner must perforce conclude that the prints have two different donors. The presence of one or more two-donor pattern dissimilarities constitutes the standard for exclusion and the examination is terminated (Thornton, 1977; SWGFAST Standards for Conclusions, 2004).

Challenge

The single two-donor pattern dissimilarity standard is rarely applied by examiners. In court cross-examination, many examiners do not know of this standard, or of its logical derivation from the uniqueness assumption. (Leo, 1998, discusses this distinction and fails to understand the logic, asserting that if the examiner has found a sufficient number of matching characteristics, two-donor pattern differences cannot occur).

Challenge

In the absence of a standard known to examiners and consistently applied, it's to be expected that examiners reach different conclusions about the same set of latent and exemplar prints: exclude or continue to compare. Evett and Williams (1996) found that skilled examiners differed in this judgment (see Chapter 8).

E. Comparison Step 5: Assessment of Amount of Agreement Between the Latent and Exemplar

The examiner's task in the last step of comparison (assuming the exemplar has not been excluded) is to establish how many features are in agreement in type and location. The more features are in agreement, the greater the similarity of the exemplar to the latent. This similarity is used in the evaluation stage of ACE, below. Counting should be a highly quantitative and objective operation. It would be, if there were objective agreement about what is being counted and how to count it.

1. Minutiae feature agreement

Every instance of a feature located in the latent (e.g., a ridge ending) that is found in a corresponding location in the exemplar counts as a single agreement. Counting up agreements is the overall measure of similarity. For most latent prints agreement is limited, because many of the features are ambiguous in type or location.

2. Ridge feature agreement

Every instance of a set of adjacent ridges in the latent of given lengths, beginnings and endings, and distances between features along each ridge-in-sequence, contributes to what Ashbaugh calls the "volume" of agreement. Ashbaugh does not offer a quantitative metric for volume. An example would be: starting with ridge #1 in the latent, distance from start point to the first event is one feature, the event is a second, the distance and path shape to the second event is a third and the event is a fourth, etc. The adjacent ridge is counted the same way. Distances and events must agree systematically between latent and exemplar ("systematically" means that distortion might shorten or lengthen all of the affected ridges in one of the prints). The total count would be the overall measure of similarity.

Both feature systems rely on good as well as poor quality evidence in a latent. The quality has to be noted during analysis, so its weight can be used appropriately during comparison.

Challenge

Textbook descriptions of ACE, such as Ashbaugh (1999) and Champod et al. (2004), do not explain how this count is performed. Leo (1998) argues that this count is very slippery. He notes that some examiners using a minutiae feature system count both the agreement in type and the agreement in the spatial location of the same feature as two different agreements. ACE does not specify how to count agreements. This is a failure in the full description of the method.

Challenge

Not every agreement is equal. If the examiner noted an ambiguous feature in the latent, or a very distorted area in which he can place only low confidence, those agreements should weigh less. ACE does not specify how to weigh these differences.

Challenge

In the absence of a quantified procedure, examiners are expected to differ and the procedure is unreliable. This result is most dramatically shown by Evett and Williams (1996). One hundred thirty highly experienced examiners were given ten latent-exemplar pairs. They were asked for each pair to judge whether it was an identification, and if so, to report the number of (Galton) points of correspondence. The critical finding with respect to comparison Step 5 was that for every pair, the examiners disagreed with each other about the number of correspondences. On one pair the number ranged from 14 to 53. (This study is described in detail in Chapter 8.) Langenburg et al. (2009) found a similar result (see Chapter 8).

5.4 The Evaluation Stage of ACE

The evaluation stage of ACE consists of two steps: the examiner makes an *objective count* of the amount of similarity between the latent and exemplar prints found in comparison and then applies a *sufficiency standard* to support one of two decisions. If the amount of agreement meets or exceeds the threshold for sufficiency, then the examiner *individualizes* the suspect's exemplar to the latent. If the amount of agreement does not reach the threshold, then his conclusion is *inconclusive:* the suspect's finger may or may not have made the latent, and the examiner cannot determine the answer from the evidence in the two prints.

A. An Objective Measure of Amount of Similarity

An objective measure of similarity is possible to construct. For example, computer algorithms underlying AFIS systems are objective measures of similarity, expressed as a match score or similarity rating between the inputted latent and the outputted exemplar. (If the AFIS manufacturers would cooperate with the profession rather than hold their algorithms in proprietary secrecy, their different similarity measurements could be made accessible, tested and validated.)

B. An Objective Sufficiency Standard

When a metric of similarity is available, experimental evidence can provide the basis for an objective sufficiency standard. For example, if a large number of latent-exemplar pairs are collected, with ground truth known for each pair, then the amount of similarity can be computed and plotted for all same-donor pairs, and all different-donor pairs. Figure 5.13 is a hypothetical graph of those results, suggested by the results of Cole et al. (2008). To the top left of the Figure the amount of similarity on a scale of 0-10 is shown on the horizontal axis of the graph, and the percentage of same-donor pairs found for each amount of similarity is shown on the vertical axis. The expected results, as plotted here, show that most single-donor pairs have large amounts of similarity, and relatively few same-donor pairs have little similarity.

The top right of Figure 5.13 shows the expected results for the amount of similarity between different-donor pairs. Most different-donor pairs have very little similarity, but some different-donor pairs share substantial similarity (as Cole's results showed).

When the two graphs are combined, as in the bottom of Figure 5.13, the results show that same-donor and different-door pairs are found over the entire range of similarity scores. This means that there is no amount of similarity that differentiates the two kinds of pairs without error. Compare this result with Figures 2.3 and 2.4, in which physical height was used to differentiate the two sexes. The result is similar: the two distributions of heights overlap, and males and females cannot be differentiated without error using a metric of height. Same- and different-donor pairs cannot be differentiated without error using a metric of similarity.

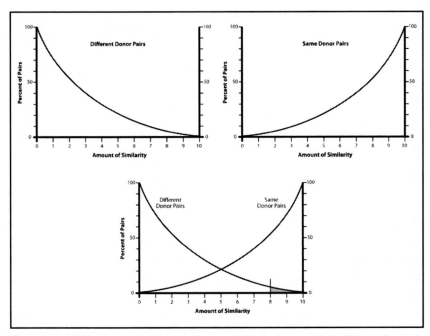

Figure 5.13 *The hypothetical results of the amount of similarity found in latent-exemplar pairs of known ground truth same and different donors. Amount of similarity is shown on the horizontal axis, and the percent of pairs is shown on the vertical axis. In the bottom of the Figure, the two graphs are superimposed, showing that for every amount of similarity, both same donor and different donor pairs are found.*

If erroneous identifications and erroneous exclusions were considered equivalent errors (comparable to the equivalence of embarrassment of confusing men with women, or women with men), then the best amount of similarity to differentiate between the two kinds of pairs is where the two graphs cross (about 5 in this hypothetical example). However, the fingerprint profession treats an erroneous identification as a much more serious error. In order to minimize this kind of error, the profession might demand much higher amounts of similarity to assert a same-donor pair. For example, in these hypothetical results, if the profession wanted to limit the erroneous identification to 2 percent or less, the sufficiency standard would be set at a similarity of 8 or above (shown as hashmarks in the bottom right of the Figure).

The fingerprint profession can set the sufficiency standard at any value. If the profession chooses to minimize the erroneous identification rate to 1 percent or less, then Figure 5.13 shows that the sufficiency standard must be set at a similarity score of 8.5 or higher. The procedure of applying an arbitrary standard to an empirical measurement of similarity produces an *objective* sufficiency standard, as the similarity metric itself is objectively defined, and the experiment underlying the hypothetical results in Figure 5.13 has been conducted and validated.

Challenge

Because this kind of experiment has never been performed, no objective basis for a numeric sufficiency standard exists.

1. Sufficiency standards in current use

In 1970, the IAI created a Committee on Identification Standards charged to document the evidence in support of a numeric sufficiency standard. The committee reported to the membership of the IAI that "no valid basis exists at this time for requiring that a pre-determined minimum number of friction ridge characteristics must be present in two impressions in order to establish positive identification" (IAI, 1973). The IAI concluded that there was no scientific support for the use of any countable standard, and that examiners could not appeal to any particular numeric standard of an amount of agreement to support a conclusion of identification.

Challenge

Until the above experiment is performed, there is no scientific basis for an objective numeric sufficiency standard. The decision to identify is left to the subjective judgment of the individual examiner.

Challenge

This experiment presently cannot be carried out, because it requires a metric of the *information content* of latent prints (to insure that prints of the full range of information are included in the research), and a metric for the *amount of similarity*. These metrics have not been developed.

Ashbaugh (2005c) has suggested an alternative method to establish an objective sufficiency standard. Every time an examiner finds ridges in agreement between a good quality latent and a known *non-match*, he makes a hard copy of the example and publishes it in a shared pool of such examples. In this way, the combined experience of examiners comprises the data of the amount of agreement needed to exceed a sufficiency threshold.

Challenge

This procedure fails to address identifications based on the poor quality latents typical of casework. Also, there is some difficulty in examiners creating a database of *known* latent-exemplar non-matches, since ground truth is not accessible in casework.

While the United States and the United Kingdom have abandoned a numeric sufficiency standard based on the number of features in agreement, most countries have retained one. Different numeric thresholds are in use, as we show in Table 5.7.

Table 5.7
Number of Minutiae Agreement Required to
Conclude Identification for Selected Countries

Germany	8-12
Switzerland	8-12
Sweden	7
Finland	12
France	16-17
Italy	16
Australia	12
Great Britain (before 2001)	16 (after 2001, none)
Canada (before 1973)	8-12 (after 1973, none)
United States (before 1973)	8-12 (after 1973, none)

2. The official IAI individual subjective sufficiency standard

The IAI in its 1973 resolution instructed each examiner to adopt his or her own standard for identification, based on his or her own personal training and experience (IAI, 1973). The SWGFAST Glossary (2003) equates identification and individualization, and defines the latter: *the determination that corresponding areas of friction ridge impressions originated from the same source to the exclusion of all others* (identification).

The suggested wording for the examiner's testimony is (Ashbaugh, 2005c), *"Based on my training and experience, I have never seen the amount of agreement present in this case from two fingerprints made by different donors. Therefore, in my opinion, the latent print found at the crime scene was made by the same person who made the exemplar fingerprints used for comparison, to the exclusion of every other person."* This subjective conclusion, based on the individual examiner's training and experience, explicitly acknowledges that the opinion being offered may not be in agreement with other fingerprint examiners, who, because of differences in their training and experience, may apply a different standard and therefore offer a different opinion.

Challenge

At present, fingerprint examiners typically testify in the language of absolute certainty. Both the conceptual foundations and the professional norms of latent fingerprinting prohibit experts from testifying to identification unless they believe themselves certain that they have made a correct match. Experts therefore claim that they make only *positive* or *absolute* identifications—they have matched the latent print to the one and only person in the entire world whose fingertip could have produced it (Mnookin, 2007).

The National Academy of Sciences Report (2009) was critical of such absolute testimony in the absence of validity data to support it. In response, Robert Garrett, President of the IAI, recently wrote: "It is suggested that members not assert 100 percent infallibility (zero error rate) when addressing the reliability of fingerprint comparisons" (Garrett, 2009). He did not indicate what alternative testimony would be acceptable.

Challenge

Neither training nor experience rests on reliable measurements. Neither the amount nor kind of training is quantified. Neither the amount nor kind of experience is quantified. Suppose I had two years of on-the-job training in fingerprint comparison. How accurate does that make me? If I had three years of such training, what would the difference be in my accuracy? If you trained as a fingerprint examiner by taking two years of courses, full-time, how would your accuracy compare to mine with two years, or three years of training on the job? The same arguments apply to experience. How can the court differentiate between 20 years of cumulative experience, and 20 years of performing the same work over and over? Does one kind of experience lead to more accurate comparison conclusions than another kind?

Challenge

In the absence of a validated metric of training and of experience, no confidence about accuracy can be derived from a description of an individual examiner's training and experience. Most training and all experience occur without knowledge of ground truth. Unless ground truth is known for a comparison, an examiner does not know whether he reached a correct conclusion. During formal training, an examiner spends some time with manufactured prints, in which ground truth is known. Most training uses casework prints, in which ground truth is surmised.

Unlike training, experience is based exclusively on casework, in which no ground truth knowledge is available. Unlike appliance repair wizard Charlie, described in Chapter 2, he receives no feedback from experience. Take an examiner who has compared thousands of latent prints, and, for some, judged identification. To assume the accuracy of every identification he made is entirely circular: "I have never made a mistake, because I was always right!"

An examiner cannot use his training and certainly not his experience to develop a standard of sufficiency, because he never knows whether his personal standard is correct.

Challenge
A subjective sufficiency standard without knowledge of ground truth is just as unreliable as a numeric sufficiency standard without experimental documentation. The profession has no scientific sufficiency standard.

5.5 The Verification Stage
Verification may be carried out for training purposes, for evaluation of skill, or to catch erroneous conclusions before they influence police decisions or court actions. The choice affects the way verification is performed. Here we are concerned only with error detection, especially when an examiner concluded identification.

Error detection involves confirmation of the examiner's conclusion by a different examiner. Verification is recommended by SWGFAST (2002a), the FBI (Budowle et al., 2006), and the Office of the Inspector General (2006), but not required. In our experience, especially in smaller laboratories, this stage frequently is omitted altogether.

When performed, two kinds of verification are possible. They have very different properties.

A. Non-Blind Verification
The most common form of verification involves an examiner taking the latent-exemplar pair to his buddy: "Check this ident." Cognitive psychologists treat this procedure as ratification rather than verification, and cite the inherent biases that make this unlikely to catch errors (Haber, 2002; Risinger et al., 2002). We discuss this expectancy bias in Chapter 9.

B. Blind Verification

Blind verification involves a second examiner carrying out a complete and independent ACE in ignorance of the work and conclusions reached by the first examiner. The acronym should be ACE-ACE. Empirical research (e.g., Arvizu, 2002; Haber, 2002) has shown that blind verifications are more likely to uncover errors.

Challenge

Blind judgments are routinely required in government testing (e.g., drug testing) and in scientific research, because the intrusion of bias when judgments are non-blind is well documented and well understood. Blind verification, while strongly recommended by the Office of the Inspector General (2006) and by Budowle et al. (2006), is rarely performed at present. When testimony is introduced in court that the identification was "verified" by another examiner, unless the verification was truly independent, that statement misleads the jury to believe that the additional step provided an additional guarantee of accuracy.

5.6 Reporting Results of a Fingerprint Comparison

...Laboratory reports generated as the result of a scientific analysis should be complete and thorough. They should describe, at a minimum, method and materials, procedures, results and conclusions, and they should identify, as appropriate, the sources of uncertainty in the procedures and conclusions along with estimates of their scale (to indicate the level of confidence in the results). (National Academy of Sciences, 2009, section 6-3)

Challenge

Fingerprint examiners are not required to make bench notes, and reports rarely include the kind of information that would make an examiner's comparison repeatable.

Challenge

We have never seen a report, or heard testimony, that acknowledged sources of uncertainty.

Challenge

Although SWGFAST promulgates three acceptable conclusions from a comparison, not all examiners adhere to them. According to the National Academy of Sciences Report (2009, section 5-11), "some latent print examiners report either 'identification' or 'negative' results. 'Negative' (or sometimes 'not identified') is an ambiguous conclusion, and it could mean excluded, inconclusive, or unable to locate after exhaustive search."

5.7 An Evaluation of ACE as a Scientific Comparison Method

We summarize the properties of ACE that fail to satisfy the requirements of a scientific method.

1. *The steps of the method must be spelled out, and their sequence defined.*

Challenge

The ACE method has not been fully described, nor has the profession agreed upon a specific version of the method. The sequence of steps has not been specified, and examiners differ in this respect. As one example, some examiners begin by laying latent and exemplar side by side, others begin by analyzing the latent alone.

2. *The comparison method must specify quantitative features*

Challenge

Research shows that examiners using ACE disagree which features are present. This means a quantitative feature description has not been achieved.

3. *A quantitative description of features-in-place must be provided.*

Challenge

Examiners using ACE presently employ different systems to assign spatial location. This means examiners will disagree with each other. The relative accuracy of these systems is unknown. The method has failed to define which system to use. None of the systems in use is quantitative.

4. *A comparison method must account for variations due to different takes of the same finger.*

Challenge

The types of distortions among takes of the same finger have not been carefully described. Examiner accuracy in identifying sources of distortion has never been published.

5. *An objective measure of the information content of a latent print must be established.*

Challenge
There is no quantitative metric of latent difficulty.

6. *An objective measure of the distinction between discrepancies (two donors) and distortions (one donor) must be established.*

Challenge
The types of distortions or predictable differences among takes of the same finger have not been carefully described. The types of discrepancies arising from different donor patterns have not been described. Examiner accuracy in making this distinction *based on the type of differences present* has never been published.

7. *An objective measure of amount of similarity between a latent and exemplar print must be established.*

Challenge
There is no quantitative metric for the amount of similarity between two prints.

8. *The profession must specify objective standards for value, exclusion and identification.*

Challenge
There are no objective standards for value, exclusion and identification.

9. *Documented evidence of the application of the method is required.*

Challenge
There are no requirements for bench notes. There are no requirements to show what method the examiner employed.

We have described three quantitative requirements for a fingerprint comparison method: objectively described features, objective measurement of features-in-place, and rules to account for distortions of the underlying features created by the way in which the fingerprint was made or processed. Based on these three quantitative components, ACE requires three quantitative measurements: the amount of information contained in the latent fingerprint; the amount of difference between the latent and exemplar; and the amount of similarity between latent and exemplar. Each measurement is used to support standards for conclusions.

ACE in its present form fails to meet the criteria of a scientific method. To the extent that its components are subjective, conclusions based on ACE are unreliable. Unreliable translates into examiner disagreement, confirmed by the available evidence. "…The ACE-V method does not specify particular measurements or a standard test protocol, and examiners must make subjective assessments throughout. In the United Sates, the threshold for making a source identification is deliberately kept subjective, so that the examiner can take into account both the quantity and quality of comparable details. As a result, the outcome of a friction ridge analysis is not necessarily repeatable from examiner to examiner" (National Academy of Sciences Report, 2009, section 5-9).

When examiners disagree about the evidence in a latent-exemplar pair, some of them must be wrong. An unreliable method is an invalid one: some conclusions based on the application of this method will be erroneous.

Chapter 6

Automated Fingerprint Search (AFIS)

What happens when the crime scene investigator finds a latent fingerprint, but the police have no suspect? Prior to the computer-accessible fingerprint databases developed in the 1980s, a diligent examiner could search manually through files of exemplar fingerprints from previous cases. The capacity to search depended on classification systems that allowed exemplars to be "binned" by similarity (McCabe, 2004). Such searches, in addition to being very slow and laborious, were limited to the files available in the particular crime laboratory. Successes were rare. As the number of exemplar files grew, these searches became an unrealistic chore.

Early automated search programs were called AFIS, an acronym for Automatic Fingerprint Identification System. While the "I" in AFIS stands for identification, no one claims (at least out loud) that these systems make identifications. The systems are designed only to *search* their database for exemplar prints that are *similar* to the latent. AFIS systems do not make identifications. A human fingerprint examiner compares the latent to the exemplars produced by the AFIS. If the examiner believes he has found a match, he may (or may not) request the original exemplar tenprints. He then may (or not) compare the original latent (not the inputted one) with them.

By 1980, the first functioning computer system was developed for the FBI, and very shortly, competing systems were developed and sold to other crime laboratories. At the time, individual crime laboratories created their own databases by inputting their own exemplar records, which their own computer could search. Figure 6.1 provides a flowchart overview of an AFIS search.

Few early AFIS's could search another system, because the algorithms were different, and the files of exemplar fingerprints were not compatible. The FBI led the way to require compatibility among the competing systems, and this permitted the multiple database files to be merged into ever larger regional and state files. Today, the FBI has a national database containing nearly a half-billion exemplar fingerprints, and many state-wide systems contain millions of exemplars. The FBI's goal is to have a single database that contains everyone's fingerprints (Holman, 2005). The current FBI system is called IAFIS: the first I stands for "integrated," indicating that different AFIS systems can talk to one another. McCabe (2004) and Komarinski (2005) provide information about the more popular systems.

Unfortunately, the acronym AFIS with the word "identification" embedded in it promotes the erroneous belief in the public, in the jury, and occasionally in examiners that the computer is accurate enough to individuate the exemplar that matches the latent print.

Current estimates made to us by many examiners suggest that about half of all fingerprint cases require the use of automated searches.

Figure 6.2 shows an AFIS output in which six candidate suspects were requested. The inputted latent is shown on the left, and the six candidates, ranked 1-6 are shown in the rest of rows 1 and 2.

In most laboratories, the AFIS technician is not a trained latent print examiner, so the AFIS technician performs the search and a latent fingerprint examiner performs the comparisons. In laboratories where the same person does both, the task-sharing is fraught with potential for bias, as we discuss at the end of this chapter.

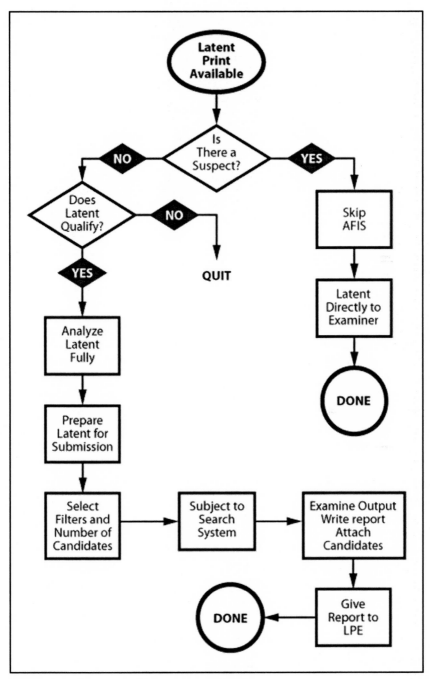

Figure 6.1 *A flow chart of an AFIS search.*

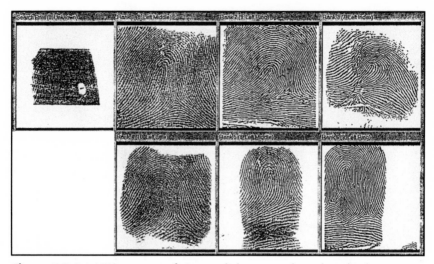

Figure 6.2 *An AFIS output of six candidates produced to the latent.*

6.1 Search Accuracy

Because AFIS is a search system and not an identification procedure, the only relevant evaluation of an AFIS system is its *search accuracy*. The search accuracy of an AFIS is its success, *if the matching exemplar is in the database*, in producing that exemplar among the output candidates.

Cole et al. (2008) provide the only non-commercial and peer-reviewed experiment on search accuracy (described in Chapter 2). They found for exemplar-to-exemplar searches that when the matching exemplar was in the database, it was produced as one of the ten candidates 79 percent of the time. For latent-to-exemplar searches, the matching exemplar was produced 82 percent of the time among the ten candidates requested. These results suggest that search accuracy is about 80 percent for the one system they tested.

Challenge

AFIS manufacturers test the accuracy of their systems in-house. Precise descriptions of these testing procedures are not accessible to purchasers or researchers. This prevents evaluation of their reported accuracy. For example, accuracy reported by a manufacturer may correspond to everyday use of the system, or may reflect artificially high quality input latents. Most manufacturers report search accuracy results substantially higher than those found by Cole et al. (2008).

6.2 Factors that Affect Search Accuracy

Common sense suggests that many kinds of factors affect search accuracy, including: (1) the quality of the original tenprints that comprise the database, (2) the amount and type of preprocessing needed to input the latent, (3) the kinds of algorithms used to define and extract similarity, (4) the number of candidates requested, (5) the size of the database, (6) the quality of the submitted latent print, and (7) the training and proficiency required of AFIS technicians (see Komarinski, 2005 for a review).

A. Quality of Database Exemplars

If the matching exemplar in the database is of poor quality, the ability of the search algorithms to find it is reduced. Historically, these databases were created at different times, in different laboratories, under varying degrees of skill. The same search system would perform differently on these different databases.

B. Preprocessing Latents for AFIS Input

In theory, an AFIS system might require little or no preparation of the latent print. The AFIS technician could use a preprogrammed scanner to enter the latent print into the system, and the AFIS algorithms could determine, without further input from the technician, its orientation, the location of the core and the relevant features on which to search for the most similar exemplars. These systems demand very high computing power. At present, most AFIS systems in crime laboratories require a human technician to mark features and/or ridge paths manually in the latent print before it can be searched.

AFIS systems differ in the kinds of preprocessing necessary. For example, some AFIS systems require the technician to trace a number of ridges. For others, the technician defines the orientation of the latent and locates its core. Then he enlarges the latent, typically at his computer station, and labels several trustworthy features in their locations. Substantial training and experience are needed to prepare latent prints for submission to this system, since the AFIS technician decides which features are trustworthy. Different technicians produce different interpretations of the same latent and the same technician sometimes makes more than one version of the same latent (National Academy of Sciences Report, 2009, section 10-2). When this latent is compared to exemplars turned up in the search, those exemplars are found because they include the features indicated in the preprocessed latent, not necessarily those in the original latent.

Challenge

There is no research that compares the accuracy and/or consistency of different kinds of preprocessing. Therefore, there is no evidence on search accuracy as a function of type of preparation, or on the consistency with which AFIS technicians preprocess latents based on tracing ridge paths or identifying features. Without this research, it is not possible for a crime laboratory to make a reasonable decision as to which system to purchase, or to evaluate the accuracy of the system they own.

C. Variation Among Algorithms Defining Similarity

Each AFIS system consists of computer-executed algorithms that compare the inputted latent to all the exemplar prints in the database, and assess the amount of similarity for each comparison. Amount of similarity is usually expressed numerically as a ranking or rating.

Because of the proprietary issues, AFIS manufacturers do not disclose the nature of these algorithms, including how features are compared and how similarity is determined. Prabhakar and Jain (2004) describe a number of similarity algorithms used in research, some of which require orientation of the print, and/ or identification of the minutiae to be compared, and/or rely on spatial similarities.

Challenge

There is no published research that compares the accuracy of different similarity algorithms for the AFIS systems in commercial use in crime laboratories. Again, purchase decisions are made by crime laboratories without the evidence needed.

Challenge

Consider a thought experiment (described anecdotally in the National Academy of Sciences Report, 2009, section 10-4): an AFIS technician preprocesses a single latent for two different AFIS systems, both of which search the same database, and he specifies that each search produce 15 candidates. The results will be two different sets of candidates, because different algorithms have been applied. Even if the same candidate were produced by both systems, their rankings are unlikely to agree. This thought experiment suggests rankings are changeable, system-specific, and unreliable.

D. Variation in the Size of the Database Searched

If the same latent is inputted into a small database, and into a large one containing the entirety of the smaller one, only some of the candidates produced are the same (National Academy of Sciences, 2009, section 10-4). If the second database is huge, there may be no overlap between the two sets of candidates. This suggests that search accuracy depends on the database size.

Challenge

The probability of a search including the correct exemplar as a function of the size of the database is presently unknown. The interaction between algorithm type and database size is unknown.

E. Variation in the Number of Candidates Requested

The number of candidates requested is up to the technician. The larger the number requested, the longer it takes the human examiner to compare each of them to the latent after the search. However, it is not known whether asking for more candidates increases the chances of finding the correct exemplar, or simply makes more work for the examiner.

Challenge

The number of candidates needed to optimize search accuracy is an empirical question which current research has not answered. It seems likely that the number would vary as a function of the type of search system employed and the size of the database.

F. Variation in the Quality of the Crime Scene Latent Print

Every AFIS System has a limit on the quality of the latent it can search. The consequences of submitting a very poor latent have not been well studied.

Challenge

There is no metric of quality (or difficulty) of a latent. As a result, there is no way to quantify which latents are too poor for the system to utilize for a search. The extent to which search accuracy correlates with quality of latent is also unknown.

G. Variation in Training and Proficiency of AFIS Technicians

With rare exceptions, there are no standards that govern the training, experience or the proficiency of the AFIS technician making the inputs to the system.

Challenge

Without training standards, there can be no assessment of performance as a function of training. In the absence of proficiency testing, the quality of an AFIS technician's work is unknown.

6.3 Individualization Accuracy Rates of AFIS

If you have been reading carefully up to here, the above heading is nonsense. AFIS systems do not make identifications, so it is meaningless to ask how accurately they make them. We raise this seemingly "empty issue" for two reasons.

A. Automated Tenprint to Tenprint Searches

Our discussion has concerned AFIS searches of exemplars with a latent print input. Frequently, the input is an exemplar tenprint. For example, the police believe that the man they just arrested may be using an alias. They can find out whether he has a record of related crimes by submitting his tenprint to AFIS. Or a customs officer fingerprints a person entering the country and compares his tenprints with tenprint cards on file from persons suspected to be criminals.

Cole et al. (2008) evaluated exemplar-to-exemplar search *identification* accuracy, using comparison of single digits. They found that the correct candidate received the highest rank 75 percent of the time (see Chapter 2 for a detailed description of this experiment). If this AFIS system was allowed to make the identification, unaided by a human examiner, it would be correct 75 percent of the time by this criterion, and erroneous 25 percent of the time. Manufacturers (much less trustworthy because the data come from in-house studies, but using all ten digits for comparison) have claimed search accuracy as high as 98 percent for tenprint to tenprint comparisons. This reported accuracy has led an increasing number of laboratories to let the computer make the identification for tenprint to tenprint comparisons, as long as the highest candidate's rating exceeds a predefined threshold. The result is not further verified. This procedure is called "lights out." AFIS is already being used as an *identification* system for tenprints. This is likely to become the direction of the future.

Challenge

No independent studies have assessed the accuracy of lights-out comparisons. No published studies have shown the effects of factors that might affect that accuracy, such as database size and number of candidates requested.

B. Biometric Identification Systems

Some forensic comparisons, including fingerprints and retinal patterns, are now performed completely by computers, with no intervention from human examiners. Biometric systems use fingerprints for identification in highly constrained contexts: everyone who is allowed access to a building has her or his exemplar stored in the database of users, and the latent print made from any person wishing to enter is precisely oriented and controlled. Ratha and Bolle (2004) contains a number of research papers on these programs. Their accuracy levels approach

100 percent when the number of exemplars (allowable users) is severely limited.

However, accuracy drops sharply when the number of exemplars in the database becomes very large, so biometric systems are not presently useful as AFIS systems. While some of the papers in Ratha and Bolle explore automatic fingerprint identification systems with unlimited databases and uncontrolled latent print inputs, their results so far suggest that human fingerprint examiners are not about to be replaced by a computer in the short term. The results of Cole et al. (2008) for latent-to-exemplar searches (see Chapter 2) support this as well.

6.4 Comparisons of Suspects Produced by AFIS are Subject to Biases that Reduce Accuracy

Current research on bias and expectancy confirmation (Risinger et al., 2002) strongly suggests that when an examiner applies the ACE method after he performs an AFIS search, he is more likely to make an erroneous identification than if he had started the comparison process without the AFIS output. At least four scientifically inappropriate practices in crime laboratories expose this examiner to bias, which increases the probability of an erroneous identification. These biases include: (1) having processed the latent; (2) seeing suspect exemplars before completing analysis of the original latent; (3) knowing the similarity ranks or ratings of the output exemplars during comparison and evaluation; and (4) reconfiguring the latent for submission when the first version fails to produce a match. These biasing factors are discussed in detail in Chapter 9.

6.5 Documentation and Discovery

AFIS procedures and the validity (accuracy) of their outputs have received relatively little attention from the profession and the courts. We outline the kinds of information that the profession needs to assure quality control for AFIS use, and that the court needs to assess the accuracy of individualizations based on an AFIS search.

A. An AFIS Procedural Manual

How can a crime laboratory insure that AFIS procedures are applied consistently and in a bias-free manner? The solution is a procedural manual, generated by the profession, which describes the use of AFIS and the application of ACE following AFIS.

Challenge

The procedures governing AFIS-based identifications are neither well defined nor well governed. The unknown accuracy of these identifications encompasses

the unknown validity of ACE, further decreased by the variation in AFIS procedures from laboratory to laboratory and the intrusion of multiple biases.

B. An AFIS Report

Whenever an AFIS search is used in a case, the AFIS technician should be required to prepare a written report that includes: (1) input instructions for the
number of candidates requested, the filters applied, if any (e.g., limit the search
to white males) and the database to be searched; (2) a copy of the original latent
print; (3) a copy of the prepared latent print; (4) the procedures used to prepare
the latent for submission; (5) if more than one prepared version of a latent was
made, a copy of each prepared latent and a description of the procedures used to
make it; (6) the complete output of the exemplar prints of all candidates and their
rating and/or ranking; (7) the name of the AFIS technician who carried out the
search; and (8) the name of the latent print examiner who carried out comparisons between the latent and the exemplars.

Challenge

We have never seen such a report.

6.6 The Unrecognized Bias in Cold Hits

Suppose a fingerprint examiner identifies an otherwise unsuspected candidate
from an AFIS output. This is called a "cold hit." If subsequent police investigation uncovers many links between this suspect and the crime (they find the stolen
money in his home, and the bank teller confidently picks him out of a lineup),
the examiner's identification changes from a "cold" to a "hot hit," because other
evidence, determined independently, points to the suspect as the perpetrator. The
probability that the suspect is the perpetrator is high apart from the fingerprint
examiner's identification.

When an examiner makes a cold hit of an AFIS candidate and subsequent investigation fails to produce other evidence of complicity in the crime, the suspect
remains a cold hit.

Cold hits have a vastly higher statistical probability of being erroneous identifications than hot hits made by the same examiner. Because this fact is poorly
understood, we offer three examples, two from forensics.

A. Three Statistical Examples

Consider first an equivalent example from outside forensics. Imagine the joy of a
birdwatcher when he reports sighting a bird way out of its normal habitat. After
consulting the guidebooks, he learns that this bird has only been seen in this part
of the country once in the past century, even with an average of 30 bird watchers

reporting every day. It is a rare find indeed, and a cold, cold hit. One sighting on one day in one century by 30 watchers is a probability of one in a million. Even so, this birdwatcher is very confident that his sighting is correct, because when he was tested for his identification accuracy in the field, he was right 99 out of every hundred sightings—an error rate of 1 percent. The question is, what are the chances that this birdwatcher made a mistaken identification in this particular instance? The bird watcher claims, from his proficiency testing, that the accuracy of this sighting (cold hit) is also 0.99. Practically a certainty. But he is wrong. He has ignored the rarity of the bird in this locale. The very low probability that the bird was really there (one in a million) reduces the watcher's probability that he identified the bird correctly from 99 in 100 to no more than 1 in 10,000 (see Aitkin, 1995, for this calculation of Bayes' theorem).

Here is another example. An empty bus was involved in a hit and run accident at night. The driver did not come forward, but a witness reported seeing the bus from a distance and it appeared to be red in color. The police narrowed their search to just red buses, and found one in the bus parking yard that had been out that night. The police tested the witness on a comparable night from a comparable distance, and found that he could discriminate colors of buses correctly 9 out of ten times (an error rate of 10 percent). Since the witness was quite accurate, the driver of that red bus that night was arrested. What about the fact that in that locale, only 10 percent of the buses were red? The odds that a red bus was involved are only 1 in 10, which reduces the witness's accuracy in picking the right bus from 9 in 10 to less than 1 in 10 (Thompson et al., 2003). With those odds, the arrested driver is unlikely to be the perpetrator, because it is so unlikely that a red bus was involved.

A third example illustrates how the same computations apply to fingerprint identifications. Assume the chances were only 1 in 1,000 that the cold hit had anything to do with the case before the fingerprint examiner identified him, and subsequently the police were unable to find any linking evidence to change those odds. Further assume that the fingerprint examiner has an error score on his proficiency tests of 1/100—he makes only one error out of 100 identifications. The odds that his identification is accurate are not 99/100 (his proficiency score), but reduced to less than 1/10, after adjustment for the unlikely chance that the cold hit had anything to do with the crime. If the examiner got an even higher score on his proficiency tests, and made only one identification error in a thousand identification cases, the probability that this cold hit is a correct identification is not 999/1,000, but still less than 50 percent.

Thompson et al. (2003) describe the statistical computation and evidence. Cold hits require far higher accuracy to produce the same probability of accuracy as hot hits. The cold hit identification constitutes misleading and very poor evidence.

Challenge

AFIS cold hits create two problems of bias. The first, described above, concerns the misrepresentation of the likelihood that the cold hit identification is correct. The second problem is different. Once the fingerprint examiner makes an identification of a cold hit, the police naturally seek evidence to confirm it, while often ignoring disconfirming evidence. A wide research literature demonstrates that confirmatory bias leads to erroneous conclusions (Risinger et al., 2002).

Challenge

With the advent of more and more computer searches and ever larger databases, the frequency of cold hits will increase steadily. Until the legal system develops rules to protect suspects indicted on the basis of a cold hit, the probability that innocent people will be convicted will increase. At present, the burden of demonstrating the extremely low probability of the accuracy of a cold hit falls entirely and unfairly on the defendant.

Chapter 7

How Good is Stella Lavie? Proficiency and Certification Testing of Fingerprint Examiners

In the first chapter of this book, following a bank robbery, a latent fingerprint examiner named Stella Lavie made an identification that led to Mr. Lightfinger's conviction. How accurate is Stella Lavie? How should her accuracy be assessed?

Error enters the equation from three sources: failures of the uniqueness assumptions, performance mistakes by the examiner, and imprecision in the method she uses. When experts in other professions testify in court, they normally rely on research evidence of population overlap (the probability that the uniqueness assumption fails, e.g., the probability that two DNA samples from different individuals will be the same), standardized evidence of the expert's own proficiency in her field, and documented scientific evidence of the accuracy of the method she used. The fingerprint profession appeals to the same kinds of evidence, the uniqueness of friction ridge skin, the accuracy level of the particular examiner and of examiners in general, and the power of the method to arrive at correct answers.

In Chapter 2 we reviewed the scant evidence that suggests that exemplars and latents are confusable with prints from other donors, a failure of the uniqueness assumptions for fingerprints. In this chapter we outline the characteristics of properly designed proficiency and certification tests to document individual accuracy levels. We then contrast the proper designs with the tests currently used by the fingerprint profession. We review the *adequacy* of the fingerprint proficiency testing programs. In the next chapter, we present the *results* of these programs and evidence of the accuracy of the ACE method.

7.1 A Brief History of Proficiency and Certification Testing of Fingerprint Examiners

In 1983, the American Society of Crime Laboratory Directors (ASCLD) set up a crime laboratory accreditation program. Central to that program was the requirement that every latent fingerprint examiner employed by an accredited laboratory be given an annual proficiency test (ASCLD, 1998). A test was created, administered and scored each year by the Collaborative Testing Services (CTS), working under contract with ASCLD. The format of this test has changed little over the years (http://www.collaborativetesting.com/forensic/report_list.html).

In those tests, participants receive a number of latent prints of unknown origin and several sets of known suspects' exemplars. The test-takers usually are permitted only two responses: identification or not identified. Copies of the test are mailed to the accredited laboratory. Each laboratory administers the test following its own in-house procedures. Some laboratories require each examiner to take the test individually, others test their examiners in groups.

From 1995 into the present, this test has also been available to individuals, whether or not they are employed in a crime laboratory, or even employed as a latent fingerprint examiner. The test is mailed to the applicant, who completes the test without proctors, and mails it back to the CTS.

Table 7.1 provides a description of the 2007 CTS Proficiency Test, as it was presented to examiners who took the test.

Table 7.1
The Scenario for the 2007 CTS Proficiency Test

Police are investigating the theft of an automobile which belongs to Spencer and Melissa Mahoney. The vehicle was found the next day abandoned on the side of the road with several belongings and the stereo missing. Investigators have supplied you with images of 11 latent prints from the vehicle and images of known prints of the two car owners and of two suspects.

The items submitted include:

- Item 1: known finger and palm prints of owner Spencer Mahoney
- Item 2: known finger and palm prints of owner Melissa Mahoney
- Item 3: known finger and palm prints of suspect Bradley Williams
- Item 4: known finger and palm prints of suspect David Berkman
- Item 5: Eleven (11) latent prints (5A-5K) recorded from the vehicle

The eleven lines of the response sheet are for the 11 latents, 5A through 5K, respectively. For each latent, mark the item number (1 through 4) in the box to which you identified the latent, and mark the finger number or palm in its appropriate box. If a conclusive identification cannot be made, check the box "Not Identified."

Some crime laboratories also develop, administer and score their own proficiency tests. The FBI carried out its proficiency testing in-house from 1995 through 2002 (described by Meagher, 2002).

The IAI certification test was first administered in 1977. The test consists of pattern interpretation of inked impressions; multiple choice questions relative to the history of fingerprints, pattern interpretation of latent prints; either oral board testing and/or presentation of a case for review to include latent print, inked print, charted enlargements and court qualifying questions and answers; participation in a mock trial; and a comparison section similar in content to the CTS proficiency tests. That part of the test has typically included 15 latents to be compared to a number of suspect exemplars. To pass the comparison section of the test, an examiner must identify at least 12 of the latent prints correctly, without making an erroneous identification.

Prior to applying for certification, the IAI requires a minimum of 80 hours of Certification Board approved training in latent print matters, a minimum of two years full-time experience in the comparison and identification of latent print material and related matters, and a Bachelor's Degree plus two years full-time experience as prescribed by the Latent Print Certification Board or (1) an Associate Degree (or documentation of 60 semester hours or 90 quarter hours of college credits) plus three years full-time experience as a latent print examiner equals the Bachelor's Degree requirement or (2) four years full-time experience as a latent print examiner equals the Bachelor's Degree requirement (IAI, 2009) (www.theiai.org).

We evaluate proficiency and certification testing in terms of *test content, scoring, statistical measures of validity and reliability, administration*, and *quality control*.

7.2 Selection of the Content of a Proficiency Test
A. Content Appropriateness
If the goal of a proficiency test is to predict how well an examiner performs in the laboratory, the contents of the test must be equivalent to normal casework.

Challenge
This content standard has never been met in fingerprint examiner testing. Proficiency and certification testing of fingerprint comparison focuses on a relatively rare occurrence in casework: each latent to be compared is of value, no AFIS search is required, and a matching suspect's exemplar usually is provided. In contrast, casework includes mostly latents of no value (i.e., much more difficult), latents requiring an AFIS search, and latents that do not match the exemplars provided. This mismatch between normal casework and the test used to predict the quality of that

work means that the results of the test cannot be generalized to accuracy in normal casework. Current proficiency and certification tests cannot serve to estimate the accuracy of an individual examiner, or of the fingerprint profession as a whole.

B. Item Difficulty Appropriateness

Some latent fingerprints are large, clear, relatively undistorted, and contain many highly informative portions. Such a latent print would be specified as extremely easy on an objective scale of easy-to-difficult. Conversely, some latents are small, fuzzy, low contrast, smeared, distorted, unclear as to orientation, and include few unambiguous features. While the fingerprint profession recognizes that this objective scale, described in Chapter 2, can be constructed (FBI, 2007), it has never been developed. The consequence for proficiency and certification tests is that the difficulty of each test item is unspecified and unknown.

Challenge

Until an objective scale of easy-to-difficult latent fingerprints has been validated and shown to be reliable, proficiency and certification test results cannot be interpreted. Results from different tests cannot be compared, and results from different years cannot be compared.

C. Skills to Be Assessed

Proficiency testing presently is designed to show whether an examiner can pass a fairly low level of comparison skill, often called a "trained to competency level" (SWGFAST, 2002b, ver. 2.1). The profession has not defined the skill level considered to be "competent." Further, the proficiency tests assess a single skill, the accuracy with which an examiner compares latent and exemplars, although other skills are required to be a proficient examiner. In contrast, the IAI's certification test assesses a range of skills.

D. Comparison Method Employed

Examiners assert they use the ACE method, so the proficiency test should assess the skill with which the examiner applies the method. This is accomplished by requiring a written ACE report, in which the test-taker documents the steps he followed in analysis, comparison and evaluation. However, no record of the examiner's work is required, either in CTS proficiency tests or in the IAI certification test.

Challenge

The contents of CTS proficiency tests are inadequate. The latent-exemplar pairs in the tests do not generalize to casework, the latents are comparatively easy, the test items lack known difficulty levels, only a single skill is tested, and no documentation of the comparison process used is required.

7.3 Selection of Appropriate Response Categories

The rules of the fingerprint profession (SWGFAST, 2002) permit only these conclusions from a fingerprint comparison: the latent is of *value* or *no value* for comparison; the suspect can be *excluded* as the donor of the latent; the suspect can be *individuated* as the donor of the latent; or the comparison is *inconclusive*.

A. Test Response Categories Do Not Correspond to the Profession's Rules

The CTS proficiency tests do not permit or assess these response categories. Typically, only one of the SWGFAST conclusions is permitted, namely, *identified*; and only one other response is allowed on the test, namely, *not identified*, a response which is not one of the four approved by SWGFAST (see Table 7.1).

The no-value response is frequently eliminated. Examiners are told that all of the latent prints in the test are of value.

Challenge

No-value latent prints are the most frequent kind of print found. This test cannot evaluate the most common judgment the examiner is required to make. This test cannot determine an examiner's accuracy in performing the first step in ACE.

Challenge

The permutation of the exclusion and the inconclusive responses into a "not-identified" category deviates from SWGFAST's regulations, from examiners' training, and from their experience. Equally seriously, not-identified is ambiguous: did the examiner exclude the latent, or was the examiner unable to decide?

Challenge

This ambiguity removes the ability of the test to determine an examiner's proficiency in making exclusions during the comparison stage of ACE.

Challenge

Examiners are trained, they practice, and all of their experience is with the SWGFAST-permitted conclusions. Until they come to take the CTS proficiency test! The non-conventional response categories make the responses to the CTS proficiency test uninterpretable and prevent generalization of the results to casework.

7.4 Statistical Standards

Two measures of the usefulness of a test are whether it measures what it is supposed to measure (its *validity*), and whether it does so consistently (its *reliability*).

A. Validity of Proficiency Testing

Validity is a scientific and statistical concept, with both a qualitative and quantitative component. The qualitative component of a valid test (usually called its face validity) is whether the test has the appearance of measuring the skill in question.

1. Face validity of proficiency tests

If the tasks to be assessed are well described, then a face-valid test asks the person to perform a sample of those tasks. A face-valid fingerprint comparison proficiency test would contain comparisons of latent prints to exemplars in which the latents were comparable in difficulty, value, distortion and the ranges of ground truth to those found in normal casework.

Another measure of the face validity of a test is the correspondence between the content of the test and the descriptions found in an authorized text or laboratory manual that spells out how the tasks are to be performed, such as a training and quality control manual on the application of the ACE method. The text description defines the content that should be included in the proficiency testing.

Challenge

The review of the content issues shows that the proficiency tests used for fingerprint examiners have very poor face validity. They do not include samples of most of the kinds of comparison tasks performed by examiners in casework, and, because they do not require the examiner to record the method he employs, no way exists to ascertain validity. Since there is no authorized training and quality control manual for the ACE method, that avenue for examining face validity is closed.

2. Correlation validity of proficiency tests

The second kind of validity is quantitative, assessed by statistical analysis, in which an examiner's proficiency test score is correlated with his scores on other measures of his proficiency, such as supervisors' evaluations, years of training, certification test results, or years of experience. The amount of correlation validity is objectively measured by the magnitude of these correlations. If proficiency test scores are in high agreement with other measures of proficiency, then the proficiency test can claim high correlation validity.

Challenge

None of these kinds of correlations has been reported for the CTS proficiency tests or any other proficiency tests used for fingerprint examiners. Correlation validity cannot be demonstrated, because the CTS does not ask those who take the test to indicate their experience, their training, courses taken or other test or examination scores. In the absence of these data, the validity of current tests for predicting the proficiency of fingerprint examiners in their casework cannot be assessed.

B. Reliability of Current Proficiency Tests

Reliability is also a statistical property of a test. When a test's reliability is high, it indicates that the score achieved by an individual can be trusted: he's likely to get the same score if he takes a comparable test again. When a test is reliable, differences in scores between individuals can be trusted to be real differences and not just chance due to measurement errors in the test. When a test is reliable, differences in scores as a function of different amounts of training or experience can also be believed. None of these is true if the test is not reliable.

Reliability is frequently assessed by making two equivalent versions of the test and then showing that people receive about the same score on both versions. Those who got a high score on version A also get a high score on version B, and vice versa. Another way, if only one version exists, is to compare the score a person achieved on the odd items of the test with his score on the even items. If the items are arranged randomly, the two scores should be about the same for a reliable test. Such data have never been reported for the CTS proficiency tests.

Meagher (2002) provided a detailed description of the FBI's internal proficiency test as part of a Daubert hearing in Federal Court, but proffered no evidence of its reliability. A number of other witnesses in that hearing testified to the statistical inadequacy of the test (Haber, 2002; Bayle, 2002; Arvizu, 2002; see also Haber and Haber, 2004). Internal evidence presented by the FBI showed that every examiner who took the test from its first year, 1995, through 2001 received a perfect score. When every test score is the same, the reliability of the test cannot be assessed (nor can its validity).

Challenge

No evidence has been published that any of the present proficiency tests are reliable. In their present forms, no reliability estimates can be suggested for these tests, since they are not constructed in equivalent multiple forms, or with equivalent items within the test. Without measures of difficulty, and of specific types of comparison tasks, the reliability of sections of the test, or the reliability of an overall score on the test, cannot be computed. Scientific journals and other scientific publications reject research lacking adequate reliability and validity estimates, because there is no scientific usefulness to the results.

1. Daubert review of proficiency test reliability

Reliability is one criterion for admissibility of evidence under Daubert. In the only review of fingerprint proficiency tests by a Federal Court (*U.S. v. Plaza* II, 2002), the court conducted a Daubert hearing on the adequacy of the CTS proficiency tests sponsored by the IAI and the ASCLD, and the in-house FBI proficiency tests. Based on the evidence presented, Judge Pollak dismissed the tests as unacceptable to a court on the grounds that these tests cannot claim to measure the quality of performance of latent print examiners, including their error rates. Cole (2005) has provided a detailed interpretation of Judge Pollak's ruling.

7.5 Administration of Proficiency Tests

Proper administration of a proficiency test requires: avoidance of potential *bias* that could be introduced when the test administrator personally knows the examiner or the examiner knows he is being tested, *uniform testing conditions, objective resolution of scoring ambiguities, random sampling* of the examiners so the results are representative of the profession whose proficiency is being estimated, and *quality control regulations* for proficiency testing.

A. Bias in Proficiency Testing

Testing research has shown that workers get higher performance scores when they know they are being tested (Arvizu, 2002). Announced proficiency testing, or the examiner's foreknowledge of the case reports to be selected for review results in artificially inflated proficiency scores.

Another source of bias arises when workers are tested by their co-workers or supervisors. A more accurate measure of performance is given when the test items are constructed, administered, scored, and evaluated by an outside agency rather than in-house.

Challenge

Nearly all fingerprint proficiency tests are administered by the laboratory and many of them are reviewed and/or scored in-house. The examiners know they are being tested.

A third bias concerns the test-taker's prior knowledge about the structure and content of the test. Most fingerprint proficiency tests use the same format year after year (for example, the FBI and CTS proficiency tests, and the IAI certification tests). To whatever extent the examiners know the structure of the tests, their decision processes become biased. They adopt different strategies and tolerances from those they use in their casework. As important examples, if the test is known to contain mostly or only latent prints of value, and when most or all the matching exemplars are known to be present, a test-taker is more likely to identify even a latent he would normally put aside as of no value.

B. Uniform Testing and Scoring Conditions

The CTS proficiency tests administered to latent print examiners are sent out and returned by mail for scoring. These proficiency tests neither control nor ascertain whether the test was taken by an individual examiner or by two or more examiners working together, or whether the responses were corrected by a supervisor in the laboratory before the test was mailed back to the testing agency.

Challenge

Currently, different examiners take the CTS tests under differing conditions. This means the test results cannot be compared from examiner to examiner.

1. The committee error correction

When an examiner takes a proficiency test alone and unaided, and records his answers on a response form that he submits to the outside agency administering the test, the score he receives is his alone. If the examiners in the laboratory normally work together, consult with each other, or routinely ask others to check their work, then it is entirely representative of the quality of that laboratory's work that they take tests that way as well. However, combining these test results significantly affects the overall erroneous identification rates.

Consider an example: Stella Lavie and Joe Moman work together in their laboratory. They submit an identification to their supervisor only if they both agree that it is an identification. Assume that on their proficiency test, which they took together, their score is a 2 percent erroneous identification rate. The 2 percent is their "committee" score. What would their individual erroneous identification rates have been if they had worked independently, as other examiners on this test did? Suppose they are of equivalent skill. In this example, 2 percent of the time they both agreed on an identification when, in fact, the two prints did not match. Under these conditions, Stella and Joe each has an independent error rate of 14 percent $(0.14 \times 0.14) = 0.02$ or 2 percent. Now assume that Stella is more skilled than Joe. Their combined 2 percent error rate reflects a 10 percent error rate for Stella and a 20 percent rate for Joe. If three equally skilled examiners worked together and their reports showed a 2 percent error rate, their individual error rates would be 27 percent ($0.27 \times 0.27 \times 0.27 = 0.02$ or 2 percent). If the committee proficiency test result is not corrected so it represents the error rate for an individual, it overestimates the proficiency of individual examiners.

Challenge
Individual and committee results are not distinguished in the scores reported by CTS. The results underestimate examiner error rates by an unknown amount.

C. Objective Resolution of Scoring Ambiguities
Just as some ballots from voters represent scoring problems, so do some responses to tests. As with ballots, decisions must be in place ahead of time as to how ambiguous responses will be treated, to avoid bias and unreliable results. One example of a fingerprint comparison scoring problem is so-called clerical error—the examiner chooses the correct suspect, but writes down the wrong finger or hand. How should this be scored? Are some kinds of clerical errors more serious than others? Clerical errors are frequently reported as correct responses. This is acceptable if there are objective criteria that define clerical error before the test is scored (K. Smith, 2002), and the number of such errors is reported. Every such scoring decision must be reported, because scoring these errors as correct unidirectionally increases the number of correct responses.

D. Sample Size and Representativeness
Whenever proficiency test scores are averaged across examiners to provide an estimate of proficiency for the profession as a whole, an adequate sample size and representative composition are essential.

1. Sample size
Almost 5,000 of the nearly 7,000 members of the IAI identify themselves as fingerprint examiners. An unknown number of non-IAI members also work as fingerprint examiners. Only a few hundred take these proficiency tests each year, or less than 10 percent of the IAI examiners.

Challenge
Generalization from small samples is much less reliable than from larger samples.

2. Sample representativeness
A more serious problem concerns which examiners take the test. If only good examiners take advantage of proficiency testing, their average scores will

overestimate the performance of the entire population of examiners. If only less skilled examiners take the test, the results will underestimate the proficiency of examiners in general. At present, information about the examiners taking the tests is not available, either with respect to their training or their experience.

Examiners working in certified laboratories generally are proficiency tested each year, in order that the laboratory maintain accreditation. This means that some component of this small sample are repeaters, sampled over and over. The test results from year to year on this small sample cannot be assumed to be independent.

Challenge
The small sample size and unknown characteristics of the examiners who take the tests prevent generalization of the results to the profession.

E. Quality Control Regulations for Proficiency Testing
An examiner who documents his proficiency during his testimony in court should be able to refer to proficiency testing quality control regulations, mandated by the profession, that show how his own proficiency testing was carried out.

Challenge
The fingerprint profession has not adopted mandated regulations.

Challenge
The administrative problems described here (testing bias, non-uniform testing conditions, inconsistent scoring, inadequate sampling and the absence of quality control requirements) each reduces the usefulness and interpretability of the proficiency test results. Most of these problems could be solved by better record keeping or by quality control regulation.

7.6 Certification Testing
The IAI Certification Test differs from the CTS proficiency tests in four important ways. There are stringent professional prerequisites to take the test, the test assesses areas of knowledge in addition to fingerprint comparison, it is considered by the profession to be a (difficult) test of excellence (IAI Certification testing, 2009), and it is administered under rigorously regulated conditions. In all other respects, it suffers from the same problems as the CTS proficiency tests.

Challenge

The items on the IAI Certification Test are easier than typical casework. All of the latents are of value and identifiable to one of the exemplars. The examiner is free to select any three of the 15 latents to set aside. Because the difficulty of the latents is not quantified, no performance level accrues to the results.

Challenge

The certification test results represent a severe sampling bias when the profession is considered as a whole. Only a small number of examiners sign up to take this test. Only examiners with demonstrated skills and experience are permitted to attempt it. These examiners are not a random sample of the profession. They are generally recognized as the best and the brightest. This means that if a random sample drawn from the entire population of fingerprint examiners took the certification test, lower individual and average performance levels would be found.

Challenge

Neither reliability nor validity measures have been reported for the test.

Challenge

Certification does not insure the proficiency of those examiners who have passed the test. Both proficiency and certification tests, in their present forms, cannot be used by an individual examiner to assure a court of his proficiency.

Challenge

Neither the individual examiner nor the fingerprint profession can demonstrate a low error rate to a court. This does not imply that fingerprint examiners are not proficient in their work, only that the tests they take do not indicate their proficiency.

7.7 Scoring and Reporting Test Results

Different scoring methods applied to the same test results produce very different kinds of information. When different scoring procedures are used for separate tests, their results cannot be compared. We illustrate this point using hypothetical data, and then describe these scoring methods in relation to the results CTS reports for their proficiency tests.

Table 7.2
Hypothetical Proficiency Test Results for Ten Latent Print Examiners

	Responses							
	Latent #A	Latent #B	Latent #C	Latent #D	Latent #E	Latent #F	Latent #G	Latent #F
LPE #1	I	I	E	IC	IC	I	IC	I
LPE #2	IC	I	IC	E	IC	I	E	I
LPE #3	IC	*EE*	IC	IC	*EI*	IC	IC	IC
LPE #4	I	I	E	E	*EE*	IC	E	*EE*
LPE #5	I	I	E	E	IC	I	E	I
LPE #6	I	I	*EI*	E	IC	IC	E	I
LPE #7	IC	I	E	IC	I	IC	IC	IC
LPE #8	IC	IC	IC	IC	I	I	E	IC
LPE #9	IC	I	E	E	IC	IC	E	IC
LPE #10	IC	I	IC	E	IC	*EE*	E	IC

I = Identification, E = Exclusion, IC = Inconclusive
EE = Erroneous exclusion, EI = Erroneous Identification

A. Results from a Hypothetical Proficiency Test

Ten examiners are given 8 latents that they are to attempt to identify to 10 exemplar ten prints. All the prints are of value. Every latent must be assigned one of these three responses: Identification (I), Exclusion (E) or Inconclusive (IC). The results for the ten examiners are shown in Table 7.2. Erroneous identifications are indicated in italics as *EI*. Erroneous exclusions are indicated in italics as *EE*. No clerical errors of any kind occurred. Latents #C, D and G were exclusions. The remaining five latents matched one of the exemplars.

The first four scoring methods described refer to the percentage of time that an error will be made, that is, that *a conclusion* will be wrong. The fifth scoring method describes the percentage of time that *an examiner* will reach an erroneous conclusion.

1. Scoring the overall error rate

The fingerprint examiner's task in this test is to discriminate between latent-exemplar pairs that share the same donor and those from different donors. What percent of the time do these examiners miss the correct answer? This score is obtained by counting the number of correct responses (I + E = 40) as the numerator. The denominator is the number of correct conclusions (40) plus the number of erroneous conclusions (6), plus the number of inconclusive conclusions (34) or 80. This shows that 50 percent of the time these examiners failed to reach the correct answer. This scoring method describes the accuracy of this group of examiners as a whole in using fingerprint comparisons to identify and exclude people.

2. Scoring the erroneous identification rate

The erroneous identification rate is found by counting the number of erroneous identifications (2) for the numerator, and dividing it by the total number of identifications (24) made (correct and erroneous) = 8.3 percent. This scoring method describes, for this group of examiners, the percentage of time that if an identification is made, it will be erroneous. The fingerprint profession frequently asserts this is the only scoring method of relevance to the Court.

3. Scoring the erroneous exclusion rate

The erroneous exclusion rate is found by counting the number of erroneous exclusions (4) for the numerator, and dividing it by the total number of exclusions made (22) = 18.2 percent. This scoring method describes the percentage of time for this group of examiners that a perpetrator will be excluded.

4. Scoring the erroneous definitive conclusion rate

Definitive conclusions refer to the combination of identifications and exclusions (Langenburg et al., 2009). The erroneous definitive conclusion rate is found by counting the number of erroneous identifications and erroneous exclusions combined (6) as the numerator, and dividing it by the total number of identifications and exclusions made (46) = 13 percent. This scoring method describes the probability, for this group of examiners, that either an erroneous identification or an erroneous exclusion will be made.

5. Scoring the responses by individual examiners

Suppose a laboratory wanted to know which examiners were the best and which needed further training. A scoring method that describes the individual examiner's performance serves this purpose. Any of the four methods just presented could be used, depending upon the information sought. As one example, consider overall error rate. Which examiners successfully identify and exclude? Which need further training? Examiner #5 reached the correct conclusion 7/8 or 87 percent of the time, examiners # 1 and #2 reached correct conclusions 5/8, or 62 percent of the time, whereas examiner #3 failed to reach a single correct conclusion, or 0 percent.

6. Scoring the percentage of time that *any examiner* (from this group of testees) will make an erroneous identification

Suppose the court wanted to know the percent of time that an examiner would attest to one or more erroneous identifications. One scoring method to describe this probability evaluates how many examiners from this group of ten testees made such an error (2). In these data, this is 2/10, or 20 percent.

B. Mis-Scoring Test Results

A considerable proportion of published experiments fail to include the number of missed identifications and/or exclusions when calculating error rate. If the purpose of the proficiency test is to evaluate examiner skill in using fingerprints to identify and exclude, all of the responses, including inconclusive ones, must be counted. For example, if only erroneous identifications are counted, a cautious examiner who rarely makes an identification will receive as high a score as a highly skilled examiner who accurately reports every identification on the test. In the hypothetical data, compare examiner #5 to examiner #8. Neither made a single erroneous identification or exclusion, but while examiner #5 was correct 87 percent of the time, examiner #8 was correct only 37.5 percent of the time. Scoring them as of equivalent accuracy misrepresents their comparative proficiency.

C. Misrepresenting Error Rate on the Basis of the Number of Comparisons Made

Examiners testifying in court often refer to the vast number of comparisons they have made, and treat that as the proper denominator—millions and millions (e.g., Meagher, 2007). They also claim that they have never made an error, so the numerator is zero, and the error rate is infinitely tiny!

The misleading aspect of this claim for the denominator is that each exemplar includes 10 digits (ignoring palm prints for this example), and every time the examiner compares a latent to a suspect, he analyzes and compares all ten. In the hypothetical proficiency test, there were ten exemplar ten prints, or 100 exemplars. If the examiner were to compare each of the 8 latents to each of the 100 exemplar digits, he would perform 800 comparisons. This is misleading because once the examiner finds the match, he searches no further. On average, this examiner would perform 400 comparisons. But this, too, is a misleading number. Many digits fail to match at Level 1 and are bypassed at a glance. The actual number comparisons each examiner performed in the hypothetical proficiency test could be established empirically. It would be far fewer than 400.

The claim of a zero error rate for the numerator is unjustified and unjustifiable. Unlike proficiency tests, in which ground truth is known, it is not known in casework. The examiner does not know how many erroneous identifications he has made, and he can never know except on valid and reliable proficiency and certification tests. Until such tests have been constructed and validated, an examiner cannot assume a zero numerator for himself.

D. Problems with CTS Scoring

We describe the CTS Latent Prints Summary Report Test No. 09-516 as an example of the problems that beset the present scoring of these tests. (The test is identical in basic format to the 2007 test presented above.) Test participants received a sample pack of twelve latent "crime scene" prints and exemplar ten prints and palm prints from four known individuals. Ten of the latents matched an exemplar, two were from different individuals whose exemplars were not provided. Only two responses were permitted: "Identified" and "Not Identified." The *only* information that can be derived from the test results is the percent of erroneous identifications made, and the percent of examiners in this sample who made one or more erroneous identifications. The overall error rate, the erroneous exclusion rate, and the erroneous definitive conclusion rate cannot be known. Nor can the relative proficiency of the individual examiners who took the test be established.

Neither the individual examiner nor the fingerprint profession can demonstrate a low error rate to a court. This does not imply that fingerprint examiners are not proficient in their work; only that the tests they take do not indicate their proficiency.

How proficient is Stella Lavie? There is no reliable way to answer.

Chapter 8

That's Your Fingerprint (Only Maybe It Isn't)! Error Rates of Fingerprint Comparisons

In the previous chapter, we described the inadequacy of current proficiency tests
to assess the skill level of an individual examiner. This chapter presents the evidence of the accuracy of individual examiners, of the overall accuracy of examiners, and of the accuracy of conclusions produced by the ACE method independent of examiner error rates.

In the first part of this chapter, we consider published evidence about the
frequency of *erroneous identifications* made by individual examiners. We attempt to use this evidence to compute an erroneous identification rate for both
individual examiners and the fingerprint profession as a whole. In the second
part, we separate errors *made by examiners* from errors that arise from the *ACE
method* itself. In the last part of the chapter, we consider evidence of the *power
of the ACE method* to produce accurate conclusions when used by highly trained
and experienced examiners.

8.1 Examiner Erroneous Identification Rates

Three kinds of published evidence provide information about erroneous identification rates of individual fingerprint examiners: (1) research results from experiments that assessed comparison accuracy; (2) proficiency and certification test
results of fingerprint examiners; and (3) evidence of erroneous identifications
testified to by fingerprint examiners in court. None of these permits a useful estimate of error rates under normal casework conditions, but each independently
suggests that performance by typical fingerprint examiners falls short of perfection.

A. Experimental Test Results as Estimates of Erroneous Identification Rates

We report results from seven experiments that assessed comparison accuracy.

1. Evett and Williams (1996)

The United Kingdom (until 2001) required that there be a minimum threshold of 16 Galton features in agreement between a latent and exemplar print for
an examiner to testify to an identification in court. Evett and Williams carried
out research on the reliability of this standard. One hundred thirty highly experienced examiners from crime laboratories throughout England and Wales (95
percent of those solicited) made comparisons of ten latent-exemplar pairs and re-

turned their results anonymously. Experts selected the pairs from Scotland Yard cases, in which all of the latents were of value for comparison, and nine of the ten pairs were identifications. Of those nine pairs, six were judged to have more than 16 features in correspondence (a full identification), two had almost 16 points (a probable identification useful for further police investigation), and one had just more or fewer than 16 (the experts who made up the test could not agree). Permitted responses were identification, probable identification, insufficient information, or exclusion. For each pair that was not excluded or judged insufficient, the respondent indicated the number of corresponding features of agreement.

No erroneous identifications were made. There were ten erroneous exclusions (0.8 percent).

Challenge

This research was neither designed nor intended to show examiner erroneous identification rates. The design included only one opportunity out of the ten pairs presented to make an erroneous identification. We include this research here only because Langenburg et al. (2009) refer to it as evidence about error rate. The two most important findings from the study, discussed below, concern the reliability of judging whether features correspond in the latent-exemplar pairs, and the very large number of missed identifications (about 50 percent).

2. The WLM training experiment

Wertheim, Langenburg and Moenssens (2006) reported error results from six different week-long training courses completed by a total of 108 fingerprint examiners. To complete the course, each examiner was required to make a minimum of 60 correct latent to exemplar identifications. Ten additional correct identifications were required for each erroneous identification reported with a high confidence level. The two permitted responses were identification and no response. Each examiner received a number of packets of prints. Each packet contained eight suspect tenprint fingerprint or palm print cards, and ten latent prints. All the latent prints were of value, and each matched one of the suspects. The ten latent prints in each packet had been judged by a skilled examiner to be of roughly the same difficulty level. The different packets covered a wide range of difficulty.

The class instructor assigned the first packet to each examiner, choosing its difficulty according to the examiner's years of experience and prior training. The instructor adjusted the difficulty level of subsequent packets to the examiner's performance. The examiner was asked to record each identification on a response form by indicating the suspect's name and finger or palm number, and to score his confidence as high (he would report the identification in casework), moderate, or low (a strong guess). If no identification was made for a particular latent, the response form was left blank (technically a missed identification, though not scored as such).

The results showed that the 108 examiners reported an average of 69.2 identifications (a total of 7,491 over all 108 examiners). The number of latent prints returned without an identification made is unknown. Of the 7,491 identifications, only 105 were erroneous, a 1.4 percent error rate. The authors made three adjustments to these data: they excluded the 16 examiners with less than one year of latent print comparison experience; they excluded identification errors they scored as clerical errors; and they excluded identification errors made with less than the highest level of confidence. The remaining 92 examiners attempted 5,802 identifications, of which all but two were correct, an error rate of 0.001 percent. The authors offered this last value as the error rate for these examiners, and argued that this research result shows the accuracy of the fingerprint profession.

Challenge

The study was a classroom training exercise, and the test contents were much easier than casework. The latent prints were all of value and all matched a suspect's exemplar (no exclusions), the examiners knew every latent was matched to an exemplar; the difficulty level of the latents was adjusted to the individual examiner's ability; if an examiner had trouble, he could ask for and receive a hint from the instructor (narrowing the search down to a single suspect); and no penalty accrued to unidentified latents, allowing the examiner to skip over ones he found problematic. Each of these choices reduced the chance of an erroneous identification. For these reasons, the WLM results cannot be used to estimate the error rate for fingerprint examiners as a profession. Haber and Haber (2006) provided a detailed critique (see also WLM's (2006) reply).

3. Langenburg, Champod and Wertheim (2009)

Forty-three expert fingerprint examiners were given the same six latent-exemplar pairs to compare. Three were ground truth same donors and three different donors, and within each ground truth class, one latent-exemplar pair was difficult, medium and easy. The examiners were given a worksheet and asked to conclude, for each pair, identification, exclusion, or inconclusive. They also reported the number of minutiae in agreement. The instructions included definitions of the three permitted conclusions and a consistent counting system for minutiae.

The experts were divided into three subgroups, in which no bias, a weak bias, or a strong bias was presented. The overall results, regardless of difficulty or bias, showed that 218 of the 257 responses were correct, or 85 percent. Of the remaining 39 responses, one was an erroneous identification (0.4 percent), 3 were erroneous exclusions, and 35 were inconclusive. Langenburg et al. count only decisive conclusions as errors, an error rate of less than 2 percent. If the authors had asked how frequently these examiners fail to discriminate between single donor and two donor pairs, the error rate is 15 percent. (We review the results for the bias manipulation in Chapter 9.)

Challenge
The difficulty of the six latents was agreed upon by three expert examiners, in absence of a quantified metric. There was no attempt to select latents comparable to casework, nor was that the purpose of the study. However, the lack of correspondence to casework latents means the error rates cannot be generalized.

Challenge
As the authors note, the participants in their study possessed a higher level of education than is traditional in the fingerprint profession. Further, they were attending an educational conference at the time—a self-selected group likely to possess higher skills and higher commitment than the average latent print examiner. This would result in artificially high scores.

Challenge
The authors also note appropriately that the participants knew they were being tested, so their performance may not reflect that of casework.

4. Langenburg (2009)
In the first phase of this experiment, six expert examiners were given a set of sixty latent fingerprints, and a set of eight exemplar finger and palm prints. The sixty latents were randomly selected from a larger set, presumably varying in quality and quantity of information (but see below). Permitted responses were identification, exclusion, inconclusive and no value. Of the 360 responses, 278 were correct (77 percent). Of the remaining 82 responses, one was an erroneous identification (0.4 percent), 3 were erroneous exclusions, 41 were inconclusive, and 37 were of no value. Langenburg counts only definitive responses as errors, an error rate of 1 percent. If the author had asked how frequently these examiners fail to discriminate between single donor and two donor pairs, the error rate is 23 percent.

Challenge
There is no evidence in this study that ACE was employed (in spite of the title of the study). Only the conclusions are reported.

Challenge

As the author observes, the difficulty level of these latents was neither quantified nor controlled. However, the author reports that most of the participating examiners completed this part of the experiment, plus a second part involving another 60 comparisons in approximately 16 hours, or 960 minutes for all 120 latent-exemplar comparisons. This is an average of 8 minutes per comparison. This brief time suggests easy latents. The results cannot be generalized to erroneous identification rates in casework.

5. Gutowski (2006)

Gutowski reported error rates from examiners in the Victoria Police Forensic Science Department based on their test results from 2000-2006 on CTS proficiency tests. Only two erroneous identifications were made, both attributed to clerical errors. On this basis, he indicates that while error rates are difficult to measure, they appear to be on the order of less than 1 percent.

Challenge

As we discussed in the preceding chapter, the CTS proficiency tests lack evidence of reliability and validity and do not correspond to casework. For these reasons, examiner error rates in casework cannot be estimated on the basis of their CTS proficiency test scores.

6. R. Smith (2004)

After examiners in the Boston Police Department Crime Laboratory made a publicized erroneous identification, the city asked Ron Smith and Associates to review the operations of the laboratory, to test the examiners to determine their strengths and weaknesses, and to provide the training necessary to return the laboratory to adequate performance levels. Smith tested these examiners on their ability to compare a number of latent prints, some rated as easy and some difficult. He asked the examiners to complete a full analysis, followed by comparison to a number of exemplars. A correct exemplar was always present. In the set of latent prints of less difficulty, 51 percent of the exemplars were correctly identified, 48 percent missed, and 1 percent erroneously identified. With more difficult latents, only 18 percent of the exemplars were correctly identified, 79 percent were missed, and 3 percent were erroneously identified.

The erroneous identification error rate was relatively low, but so was the correct identification rate. For difficult latent prints, percent of correct identifications decreased sharply (to 18 percent), although the correct exemplar was present. These results, based on a very small number of examiners known to need additional training, obviously cannot and should not be generalized to an error rate for the profession as a whole. However, they were made by working examiners in a large police department. Like the Evett and Williams (1996) results, they indicate a very low rate of erroneous identifications purchased at the cost of a very high rate of missed identifications.

7. Meagher, Budowle, and Ziesig (1998)

The results of this unpublished experiment (discussed in a different context in Chapter 2) involved automated searches carried out by a computer, not human examiners. A database of 50,000 different left loop exemplar (scanned) fingerprints was created in an AFIS. The AFIS compared each of these exemplars to the entire database. The system rated the similarity of each exemplar to itself (50,000 *same* comparisons), and to the remaining 49,999 different exemplars (2.5 billion *different* comparisons). After those comparisons were made, the authors masked part of each exemplar, leaving about 20 percent exposed around the core area (the average size of a latent fingerprint of value). They submitted these 50,000 masked exemplars to the 50,000 full exemplars, and got back a new set of 50,000 similarity ratings for the same comparisons and 2.5 billion different comparisons.

For both the full exemplar comparisons and the masked exemplar comparisons, the same comparisons received astronomically high similarity scores, while the different comparisons received much lower similarity scores. These results have been interpreted as showing that the comparison of two fingerprints would always lead to correct identifications if the two prints were the same, and to exclusions if the two fingerprints were different.

Challenge

A number of scientific reviews of this study (e.g., Stoney, 2001; Cole, 2004; Kaye, 2003) have argued that the results are irrelevant and inapplicable to the accuracy of casework fingerprint comparisons. This experiment compared two *identical copies* of the same print, not *two different takes* of the same finger, as in casework. For the latent to exemplar comparisons, the latent is usually is not the central, most informative area. This means the manufactured "latent" did not correspond to a real latent, just as the "comparison" involved identities, not different takes of a finger. The results do not pertain to the accuracy of fingerprint comparisons, either by computer or by human examiners.

Challenge

None of the seven experiments just cited can be used to indicate an error rate for fingerprint comparisons performed by fingerprint examiners under normal working conditions. We know of no other relevant experiments.

B. Proficiency and Certification Test Results as Estimates of Error Rates

In theory, Stella Lavie could document to the court her erroneous identification rate by producing her personal proficiency test results (and certification test results if she is certified). In addition, in theory, an error rate for the profession as a whole could be established from the published results of proficiency tests administered to large, representative samples of the profession. We described in the previous chapter the deficiencies in current proficiency and certification tests that make these tests results uninterpretable as error rates. Here, we present the actual results of those tests.

1. Proficiency tests and their results

From 1981-1992, Collaborative Testing Services (CTS), a private company, created and administered proficiency tests for latent print examiners. From 1993 through the present, CTS has worked with the American Society of Crime Laboratory Directors (ASCLD) to design these proficiency tests. Peterson and Markham (1995) report crime laboratory proficiency test results from 1983 to 1991. Their estimate of the average examiner erroneous identification rate over that time period was 2 percent. Vokey, Tangen and Cole (2008) provide a more detailed analysis of just the 1995 scores, and report an erroneous identification rate of 11 percent. Summary proficiency test results from 1993 through 2001 were presented by K. Smith (2002). Cole (2005) reviews these data and extends them through 2003. From 1993-2003, Cole finds an average examiner erroneous identification rate of about 5.5 percent. From 2004 onward, summary test results from various years are available online from the CTS website. Overall, the erroneous identification rates are very small (CTS website). Gutowski (2006) reports the results from a single crime laboratory of 13 examiners who took the CTS tests between 2000 and 2006. While these results suffer from all of the interpretative problems described above, they were very high. Of 782 comparisons, only two were false positives (reported to be clerical errors), none were false negatives, and seven were not identified.

2. Certification tests and their results

The IAI certification test was first administered in 1977. From 1977 through early 2009, over 1,700 fingerprint examiners have taken the test, of whom 930 have passed, a failure rate of 46 percent. Since the end of 2005, the time limit was lengthened, and the average failure rate has dropped to 28 percent.

Challenge
In the absence of a measure of test item difficulty, it is unknowable whether this improvement is due to better trained examiners, increased time, or easier test items.

K. Smith (2002) reported that the fingerprint comparison section has been the major source of failure. However, the breakdown of the test data has not been published, so an estimate of an erroneous identification rate based only on the comparison section cannot be computed.

Even if the profession were to publish a breakdown of the comparison portion of the test, for all of the reasons described in the previous chapter, the results would not provide an estimate of the individual examiner's erroneous identification rate.

Challenge

Neither the fingerprint profession's proficiency tests nor the certification tests can be used to indicate an error rate for fingerprint comparisons performed by examiners under normal working conditions.

C. Erroneous Identifications Made in Court

If we knew the number of erroneous identifications made in court, and we knew the number of cases that hinged on fingerprint evidence, then their ratio would provide an estimate of the erroneous identification rate testified to in court. We start with what is known about the frequency of identification conclusions offered in court that are later discovered to be erroneous.

1. Frequency of erroneous identifications

Cole (2001, 2005) and Haber and Haber (2004, 2007) collected all of the published examples they could find of court-attested erroneous identifications, including their verifications by fingerprint examiners. The 22 cases in which 61 erroneous identifications were made are displayed in Table 8.1. Cole (2005) suggests that the true number of erroneous identifications must be much greater.

Examples of court-attested erroneous identifications cannot be used even to estimate the numerator to compute an erroneous identification error rate for examiners. These few instances of court-attested erroneous identifications can be used, however, to belie the claim that fingerprint examiners never testify to an erroneous identification in court.

2. Frequency of cases hinging on fingerprint evidence

The denominator of the ratio of errors to total cases is also unknown. The criminal justice system does not keep its records by kinds of evidence. To make it more complicated, Altschuler (2003) estimated that fewer than 10 percent of the felony indictments in the United States were tried before a jury. In nearly all felony cases, the defendant pled guilty or pled to a lesser crime, so that no trial occurred in which a fingerprint examiner testified. This fact would vastly distort the frequency data even if they were available. A computation of an error rate for fingerprint conclusions based on court data cannot be performed.

Table 8.1
Instances of Erroneous Identifications Attested to by Fingerprint Examiners in Court. Extracted from Cole (2005) and Haber and Haber (2006).

#	Victim	Year	Jurisdiction	Crime	# Exam- iners
1	Robert Loomis	1920	Pennsylvania	Murder	2
2	William Stevens	1926	New Jersey	Murder	3
3	John Stoppelli	1948	California	Narcotics	1
4	Roger Caldwell	1982	Minnesota	Murder	3
5	Anonymous	1984	Midwest	?	1
6	Michael Cooper	1986	Arizona	Rape	2+
7	Bruce Basden	1987	No. Carolina	Murder	1+
8	Maurice Gaining	1988	No. Carolina	Burglary	2+
9	Joseph Hammock	1988	No. Carolina	Larceny	1+
10	Darian Carter	1988	No. Carolina	Larceny	1+
11	Leville Lee	1991	England	Rape	1+
12	Martin Blake	1994	Illinois	Murder	1
13	Andrew Chiory	1997	England	Burglary	3
14	Danny Namee	1998	England	Murder	2+
15	Shirley McKie	1999	Scotland	Perjury	4
16	Richard Jackson	1999	Pennsylvania	Murder	3
17	Anonymous	2000	England	?	3
18	David Asbury	2002	Scotland	Murder	4
19	Kathleen Hatfield	2002	Nevada	Investiga- tion	1
20	David Valken- Luduc	2003	Utah	Murder	1
21	Stephan Cowans	2004	Massachusetts	Murder	4
22	Brandon Mayfield	2004	U.S.-FBI	Terrorist	4

8.2 The ACE Method's Erroneous Identification Rate

A. Erroneous Identifications: Examiner or Method?

We have just reviewed evidence showing that examiners produce erroneous identifications in their comparison work. FBI Agent Meagher has testified in court (2002) that all erroneous identifications are due to *examiner* mistakes, and that the ACE *method* is error-free. He attributes examiner mistakes to insufficient training and/or experience, and sometimes carelessness (Meagher, 2003). Two recent publications by the FBI reiterate this statement (Stacey, 2005; Budowle et al., 2006).

This claim is contradicted empirically (Cole, 2005; Haber and Haber, 2007; Office of the Inspector General, 2006). For example, the highly publicized FBI erroneous identification of Brandon Mayfield (discussed in the next chapter) was made and verified by four of the most trained, experienced and skilled examiners working in the profession today (Office of the Inspector General, 2006).

In this part of the chapter, we review experimental evidence of the validity of the ACE method itself, and we review experiments and other data in which highly trained and experienced examiners made mistakes.

B. Experimental Tests of the Error Rate of the ACE Method

A pure test of the accuracy (validity) of the ACE method, ruling out examiner errors, requires a careful experiment. The test materials consist of a wide range of latent fingerprints typical of casework, paired with exemplar prints for which ground truth is known. As in casework, many of the latent prints are of no value for comparison and most of the remainder do not match their paired exemplars. Skilled examiners then carry out the comparisons. The number of erroneous identifications made represents the error rate of the method.

However, four conditions must be met to conclude that this result is a method error rate, independent of other sources of error. These are: (1) the method must be precisely described so that examiners agree on its steps; (2) the examiners must document each step to assure that they are following the method; (3) the examiners must have demonstrated maximal levels of training, experience and skill in fingerprint comparisons; and (4) the latent print used in each comparison must be specified in terms of its quality and quantity of information (its difficulty). Under these conditions, errors can be attributed to the comparison method itself.

Haber and Haber (2004), Cole (2005), Budowle et al., (2006) and Haber and Haber (2007) searched in vain for a published experiment demonstrating the validity of the ACE method. Haber and Haber (2007) described the conditions necessary to run such experiments in greater detail. They concluded that with the present state of knowledge in the fingerprint profession, such experiments cannot be conducted.

1. Why validity experiments matter

Suppose a woman needs to know whether she is pregnant (in the same way that a court needs to know whether it was the defendant who touched the gun trigger). She goes to a specialist (the equivalent of a fingerprint examiner), who performs a pregnancy test (a fingerprint comparison). The outcome of the pregnancy test might be: yes, she's pregnant. Further, the test has a known (experimentally validated) 3 percent probability of making an erroneous pregnancy conclusion. Three percent of the time this test concludes she's pregnant when she's not. This is equivalent to an erroneous identification rate of 3 percent. These data are available for pregnancy tests, but not for forensic fingerprint methods.

Challenge

The necessary research on the error rate of the ACE method has never been performed. The examiner cannot point to research that supports the accuracy of the comparison method. Would a woman act on the results of a pregnancy test if she was informed the error rate was 25 percent, or 50 percent, or worse, an unknown percent? The consumer of a fingerprint comparison method, the criminal justice system, does just that: it acts on the results of a test without a known error rate.

C. Research Evidence Showing Examiner Inconsistency

A number of research studies have found examiner disagreements during each of the analysis, comparison, and evaluation stages of the ACE method. Some studies have shown that different examiners describe the same latent print differently, or reach different conclusions for the same latent-exemplar comparison. Some studies have shown that individual examiners at different times reached a different conclusion about the same latent-exemplar pair.

When examiners disagree during analysis or comparison, they are likely to reach different conclusions. When examiners disagree with one another or with themselves about an identification in the evaluation stage, one of their conclusions is wrong. Evidence of inconsistency cannot be used to establish an erroneous identification rate, but it serves as a powerful indicator that errors occur. When inconsistencies are found among highly trained and experienced examiners, they point to failures in the method, not the examiners. We summarize results from nine studies here.

1. Analysis stage: R. Smith's value/no value tests

R. Smith (2004) tested examiners' ability to distinguish between latent prints of value and those of no value, using easy latents. For latent prints deemed by the test manufacturers to be of value, the examiners correctly judged 82 percent to be of value, and incorrectly discarded 18 percent as of no value. For the latent prints deemed to be of no value by the test manufacturers, the examiners correctly rated 87 percent of no value, and incorrectly labeled 13 percent to be of value.

These results suggest that these working examiners make about 15 percent errors on a value/no value conclusion for relatively easy latent prints.

2. Analysis stage: Langenburg's (2004) test of Galton feature labeling

Langenburg (2004) trained experienced examiners to identify and locate Galton features in latent prints. He then asked them to examine 14 latent fingerprints and mark down the number of Galton points they found in each latent. If Galton features are unambiguously defined, examiners and novices alike should always agree on the number present.

Figure 8.1 shows the number of Galton features found by working examiners for each of the 14 latent prints. The most variable latent had a range of 2 to 14. Langenburg reported that certified examiners were just as variable as non-certified working examiners. Langenburg's results show that examiners do not agree whether the basic features are present or absent in latent prints.

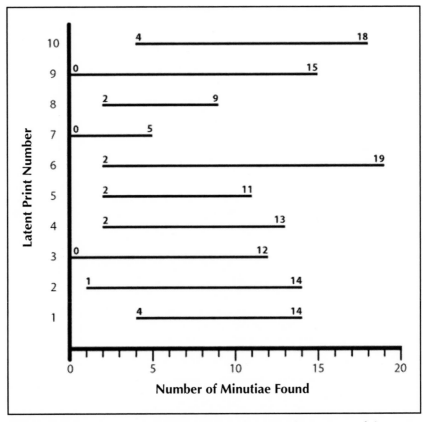

Figure 8.1 *Data from Langenburg, 2004, showing the ranges of the number of minutiae found by working examiners in each of 10 latent prints.*

3. Analysis stage: Black's (2006) simultaneous latent study

A simultaneous latent is defined as an impression containing two or more prints from different fingers of the same donor made at the same instant in time. The Massachusetts Supreme Judicial Council ruled (*Commonwealth v. Patterson*, 2005) that there was inadequate evidence under Daubert requirements to support the application of the ACE method to simultaneous latents. In response, Black (2006) reported a study to determine whether latent fingerprint examiners can successfully discriminate between simultaneous and non-simultaneous latent prints.

Black asked 31 trained examiners to analyze 30 latent impressions, each of which included multiple fingerprints. Eighteen of the latents were manufactured as simultaneous (true) and 12 were not (false). For each latent, the examiner was asked to conclude true, false, or inconclusive if he could not tell. The results are shown in Table 8.2.

Table 8.2
Number of Correct, Erroneous, and Inconclusive Responses, for True Simultaneous (TS) Impressions and False Simultaneous (FS) Impressions

	Number of Responses				
	Conclusive Responses		Inconclusive Responses		
	Correct	Erroneous	Sum Conclusions N	N	Total
TS (N = 18)	335	60	395	163	558
FS-(N= 12)	260	23	283	89	372
Total (N= 30)	595	83	678	252	930

Number of stimuli indicated by N. Number of examiners was 31. All data taken from Black (2006).

Of the 678 conclusive responses, only 83 were erroneous. From these, Black reported the error rate as $83/678 = 12$ percent. However, this misrepresents Black's purpose—can examiners "successfully determine whether two or more latent impressions are deposited at the same time." The answer to this question requires consideration of all $31 \times 30 = 930$ responses. Of these, only 595, or 64 percent, were correct. Of the remainder, 252 were inconclusive (27 percent) and 83 were erroneous (9 percent). In over one-third of their analyses (36 percent), these examiners could not successfully determine whether the prints were simultaneous.

Challenge

When potentially simultaneous prints are found in casework, a critical component of the analysis stage of the ACE method is to determine whether the latent is in fact simultaneous. A woman who wants to know whether she's pregnant would not bother to take a test for which 36 percent of the results were inconclusive or erroneous.

4. Comparison stage: Evett and Williams (1996) agreement of Galton features

We described the parameters of this experiment in the beginning of this chapter. The authors found substantial disagreement among the 130 examiners as to the number of Galton points in correspondence in each latent-exemplar pair. Figure 8.2 shows the number of corresponding points reported for three of the pairs which the manufacturers of the test agreed were *full identifications*. For pair F, the examiners reported a range of 14 to 56 features in agreement.

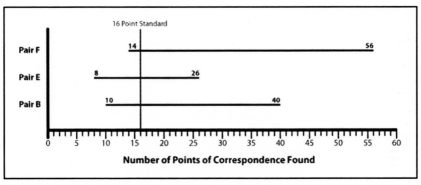

Figure 8.2 *Data from Evett and Williams, 1996, showing the number of corresponding points reported for three pairs that were full identifications.*

Variability among such skilled examiners means that the number of points found in agreement is unreliable. The method fails to define features reliably (see Langenburg, 2004, above) and fails to define agreement among features in a latent-exemplar comparison.

5. Comparison stage: Langenburg, Champod and Wertheim (2009)

We described the parameters of this experiment above. The authors report the number of minutiae the 43 skilled examiners found in agreement in the three same source pairs (they fail to report the results for the different source pairs, the very data Ashbaugh seeks to establish a criterion for sufficiency (Chapter 5)). As in the Evett and Williams study, a wide range of reported corresponding minutiae was found, indicating a high level of unreliability. Overall, the smallest difference in range was 8, the largest 21.

6. Evaluation stage: Evett and Williams (1996) conclusion disagreements

Examiners in the study were also asked to record their conclusion for each of the ten latent-exemplar pairs. No erroneous identifications were made in the study. However, the examiners differed in their conclusions about all ten pairs. The responses for the single exclusion pair were divided between exclusion and insufficient detail to make a conclusion. Consider pairs E and H, both of which were classified as full identifications by the manufacturers of the test. For pair E (shown in Figure 8.2) fewer than half the examiners (47 percent) found 16 or more points in agreement. The remaining examiners were divided between a probable identification (45 percent) and insufficient detail to conclude (8 percent). For pair H, no examiner found 16 or more correspondences: more than half (54 percent) concluded a probable identification (8-15 points); and the remaining examiners were divided between insufficient detail (38 percent) and exclusion (8 percent). Here is a pair judged by some examiners to be an identification (probable), and by others an exclusion.

Overall, the test manufacturers considered there were six or seven full identifications. Thirty-six examiners (28 percent) found four or fewer. This suggests that examiners are very cautious about making identifications. The result is a large number of missed identifications.

7. Evaluation stage: Langenburg's (2009) performance study of the ACE-V process results

In phase 1, skilled examiners compared eight exemplar sets to 60 latents. Langenburg scored these results for their consistency. He found full consensus for 43 of the 60 comparisons (72 percent). He reports that 10 of the remaining 17 trials, or 59 percent, demonstrated disagreement in sufficiency. Some examiners reached conclusive opinions, others did not. Four of the six participants had received the same training. Langenburg comments that the differences in perceived sufficiency cannot be explained by the participants' training or years of experience, as was also found in the Evett and William's study and in Langenburg et al. (2009). In one of the remaining trials, examiners disagreed as to whether the conclusion should be identification or exclusion. These findings indicate unreliability in the method.

In the third phase of his experiment, Langenburg re-presented 4 to 12 weeks later all errors made in phase 1 (and some from phase 2) to the examiner who had made the error. Forty-nine trials were re-presented, in which errors were mixed in with correct conclusions. The author's purpose was to show which erroneous identifications were clerical errors. He used a flawed procedure. Instead of a latent and a stack of exemplars, now the latent was given side-by-side with a single digit exemplar. If an examiner had chosen the right suspect, but listed the wrong finger, now he sees the latent and *wrong exemplar* side-by-side, and readily labels it an exclusion. (The correct exemplar, not shown in the re-presentation, is necessarily missed.) Langenburg unjustifiably treats such corrections as evidence that the original error was clerical.

8. Evaluation stage: FBI's Mitchell survey results

Byron Mitchell was tried in federal court (*U.S. v. Mitchell*, 1999) for allegedly driving a getaway car in a robbery. Two latent fingerprints were found on the gearshift lever, which an FBI examiner identified to Mr. Mitchell's exemplar prints. When the defense challenged the FBI's identification on the basis of lack of evidence showing fingerprint identification accuracy, the FBI offered a demonstration. They mailed a packet containing Mr. Mitchell's tenprint card along with the two latent prints found in the car to 50 different crime laboratories in the U.S. The FBI asked each laboratory to have its most experienced examiner compare these latents to the exemplar and indicate his conclusions. Thirty-nine laboratories responded. Thirty reported that they identified both latents to Mr. Mitchell, nine identified only one or neither to Mr. Mitchell. Twenty-three percent of these experienced examiners disagreed with the FBI conclusion of identifications for both latents.

9. Evaluation stage: Dror's experiments assessing effects of bias

Two experiments using highly skilled working examiners show that extraneous information influences examiners, and increases the number of erroneous conclusions they reach. (These are described in more detail in Chapter 9 on contamination effects.)

Dror, Charlton and Peron (2006), using pre-selected examiners, obtained from the previous casework of each examiner a latent-exemplar pair that he had judged an identification at least five years previously. When this same pair was presented again (none of the examiners recognized them as familiar), each examiner was told that the latent was from a notorious case of an erroneous identification. Four-fifths of the examiners now concluded either exclusion or uncertain. Only 20 percent reiterated their initial (presumably correct) identification.

In a second experiment, Dror and Charlton (2006) used a larger sample of latent-exemplar pairs. From each of six examiners' past casework, they picked pairs in which half of the pairs had been previously identified and half excluded. The pairs were presented anew to the same examiners who had compared them five years ago (none recognized the pairs as familiar), but with extraneous information that served to confirm or contradict the examiner's former conclusion. The information given influenced the examiners' current conclusions in predictable ways. Two-thirds of the examiners changed their previous conclusion (this occurred more frequently with the more difficult latent prints).

In both experiments, Dror's results show that examiners can be made to disagree with themselves by extraneous information given to them when they repeat the examination years later. Disagreements or changes in decisions about the same pair indicate that at least once, the examiner made an error on that pair.

Challenge

The studies we have reported here document examiner disagreement in every step of the ACE method. Whenever disagreement occurs, only one answer, at most, can match ground truth. Inconsistency means that examiners are making mistakes. Since the examiners tested in these experiments were all highly trained and experienced, these results implicate errors inherent in the ACE method, not in the skill of the examiner.

Challenge

When an examiner is asked in court whether there is research evidence about the error rate of the ACE method, the correct (true) response is, No, and that the error rate is not known.

8.3 The Power of the ACE Method to Identify Criminals

The FBI, in its *Science of Fingerprints* (1988, p. iii), claims that "criminal apprehension by means of fingerprints is one of the most potent factors in obtaining the apprehension of fugitives."

A. Distribution of Conclusions from ACE

Fingerprint examiners, whom we have asked, estimate that in casework about 75 percent of all crime scene latent prints are judged to be of no value. Of the 25 percent that survive to be compared to suspect exemplars, examiners estimate that over 90 percent are exclusions (or 22.5 percent of all latents). This leaves only about 2 percent of all latent prints that can draw an identification or inconclusive conclusion. We apportion this 2 percent from the Evett and Williams (1996) experiment, in which all the latent prints were of value, and 90 percent of the pairs should have produced identification conclusions. However, the examiners divided the identification and inconclusive conclusions 50-50. Using this as an estimate, 1.0 percent of all latent prints examined by the ACE method are identified, and 1.0 percent are inconclusive. Some unknown percentage of the 1 percent of identifications serve to eliminate persons who are not criminals. Figure 8.3 illustrates these distributions.

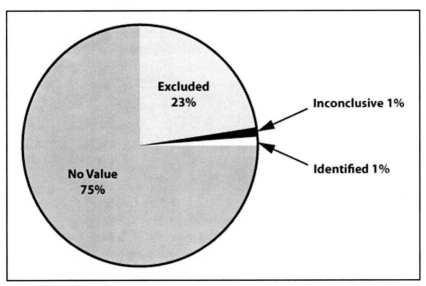

Figure 8.3 *Estimates of the percent of conclusions reported in case-work that are no value, exclusion, identification and inconclusive.*

The distributions of conclusions shown in Figure 8.3 suggest that the ACE method is not very powerful as a forensic technique for solving crimes. Only a small fraction of crime scene latents, less than 1 percent, turn out to be identifiable to a criminal suspect by the application of the ACE method.

B. Interaction Among the Four Conclusions

The fingerprint profession has focused on the accuracy of exclusion and identification judgments and paid little attention to the value/no value and inconclusive judgments permitted by the ACE method. These judgments also have serious consequences in real life: either an innocent suspect remains at risk of indictment and conviction, or a guilty perpetrator remains at large.

Table 8.3 shows the classification of the four conclusions as a function of ground truth. Correct conclusions are in bold face.

Consider the first two lines of Table 8.3. The no value and inconclusive judgments always miss the correct answer, whether the prints came from one donor (identification is the only correct answer) or from two donors (exclusion is the only correct answer).

Identifications and exclusions as a function of ground truth are shown in the last two lines of Table 8.3.

Table 8.3
The Four Conclusions Allowed by ACE, with Their
Correctness as a Function of Ground Truth

Conclusion	Ground Truth	
	One Donor	**Two Donors**
No Value	Missed Identification	Missed Exclusion
Inconclusive	Missed Identification	Missed Exclusion
Exclusion	Erroneous Exclusion	**Correct Identification**
Identification	**Correct Identification**	Erroneous

One factor that affects an examiner's conclusion are the consequences if he makes a mistake. If the fingerprint examiner will be heavily penalized for an erroneous identification, he will demand more information from the latent and a careful application of the method before he is willing to commit to an identification. If an examiner is very cautious in making an identification, he will erroneously conclude no value, exclusion or inconclusive for most of the comparisons for which ground truth is a single donor—his caution produces many missed identifications.

Referring back to Table 8.3, the cautious examiner who makes mostly no value, inconclusive and exclusion conclusions (the first three rows) *necessarily* makes fewer identifications. Consequently, any claim that the only error that counts is an erroneous identification is incorrect. Minimizing erroneous identifications inevitably increases other kinds of errors which erroneously exclude a guilty person. Erroneous identifications cannot be considered alone when computing error rates. As the National Academy of Sciences Report (2009, section S-9) phrased the issue, "In addition to protecting innocent persons from being convicted of crimes they did not commit, we are also seeking to protect society from persons who have committed criminal acts."

Challenge
The data we have presented cumulatively suggest that examiners make few identifications, at the cost of many missed identifications.

Chapter 9

Contamination in the Crime Laboratory

In March 2004, a senior examiner in the FBI fingerprint crime laboratory identified a latent fingerprint sent to them by the Spanish police to an exemplar from a U.S. citizen named Brandon Mayfield. A second senior examiner verified the identification. A third senior examiner under contract to the FBI confirmed the identification. Based on the three examiners' identification, the FBI asked a Federal Court to hold Mr. Mayfield. The court complied after a fourth examiner appointed by the court also concluded that it was Mr. Mayfield's print.

Several weeks later the Spanish police notified the FBI that they had identified the latent print to a known terrorist in Spain. The FBI looked again at the comparison and saw that they had made a mistake. The error was discovered entirely by a very rare circumstance: *independent examinations were carried out by two unrelated crime laboratories.*

How can a highly skilled examiner make an erroneous identification? How can two highly skilled FBI examiners verify as correct an erroneous identification? How can yet a fourth examiner agree with the error? Isn't this improbable beyond belief?

The FBI has carried out several investigations (Stacey, 2004; Budowle et al., 2006). An independent, detailed investigation was carried out by the Office of the Inspector General of the Justice Department (2006). Their reports concluded that all of these examiners worked under conditions that exposed them to biasing information. This bias led the first examiner to make an erroneous identification and prevented all three verifiers from seeing it was erroneous.

9.1 Expectation and Mindset

Research carried out by cognitive psychologists over the past half century has shown that normal human processes of perception, memory and judgment start from incomplete sensory information. This makes them top-down processes in which the perceiver fills in missing information based on expectations of what must have been present or should have been present in the incomplete stimulus. Here's an example from a recent case where expectations dictated what witnesses "saw" (Table 9.1).

Expectations led these witnesses to perceive a complete scene when they only saw a small part of it.

Table 9.1
The Power of Expectancies

John was standing in the doorway of an office trailer watching cars coming down the eastbound elevated exit ramp of an interstate opposite the trailer. From the door of the trailer, only about 200 feet of the descending ramp were visible. The rest of the ramp was blocked by buildings. The exit ramp had a three-foot high concrete crash wall along the side closest to the trailer, preventing view of the lower portions of vehicles on the exit ramp.

Suddenly, John shouted, "accident!" Sarah looked up and out the window in front of her desk, Peter stood and walked four feet to the nearest window, and Mary walked 15 feet to join John at the door. All four testified that they heard a loud crash and saw a garbage truck strike the rear end of a small car. John said he saw the truck traveling at high speed on the ramp just before the collision, saw it hit the much slower car from behind, saw the truck ride up into the trunk of the car, pressing the car down against the pavement, and he saw the two vehicles continue down the ramp locked together. Mary also said she saw the truck overtaking the car and hit it. All of them reported seeing flames from the small car, which increased as the trucked pushed the car down the ramp. When the interlocked vehicles came to a stop at the merge at the bottom, these witnesses all said that the car and the front of the truck were engulfed in flames.

The physical evidence showed that most of these eyewitness reports could not have been based on what the witnesses saw. All but the last 25 feet of the truck's travel before the collision were blocked by buildings, so the truck was invisible until 1/4 second prior to the collision. This is not sufficient time to perceive the speed of the truck. John could have been looking at the exact point of impact by chance (he said he was not), but if he was looking elsewhere, he could not have moved his eyes to that point fast enough to see what happened there. He might have heard the crash (200 feet away or 1/5 second delay), but by the time he heard it, it had already occurred. Since all but the window tops and roof of the small car were blocked by the crash barrier, John could not have seen the bumper of the truck (which did not reach three feet off the pavement) crash into the trunk of the car, and could not have seen the truck ride up into the trunk pressing the...

continued...

Table 9.1 (continued)

car down against the pavement. Given the time it took the other three
witnesses to orient to the location of the accident, the collision itself
was long over and they could not have seen it. Finally, the location
of the final resting place of the two vehicles, still locked together and
burning, was out of sight. It became visible only after the four witnesses
traveled 150 feet from the trailer to the frontage road.

    All four witnesses gave their reports within a half hour; all swore
they saw the entire event.

Most expectations come from prior experiences with comparable stimuli. If
you've grown up with very large, loving dogs, you treat large dogs you meet as
friendly. If you grew up without pets, you are likely to think a humongous dog
looks dangerous. You also acquire expectations from what you've learned from
other people. For example, if my good friend tells Lyn he met a great horticultur-
ist she'll like, Lyn expects to like this person and will not notice his irritating per-
sonality when they meet. (See the marvelous yet scientific book called *Mistakes
Were Made, but Not by Me*, by Tavris and Aronson, 2006.) In most instances,
your expectations serve you well, because they are consistent with the true state
of the world.

Expectations also affect you negatively. You fill in events that you did not
see, as the four witnesses did, and sometimes those filled-in events did not happen. You fail to perceive and remember information that is inconsistent with your
beliefs. You ignore contrary information. As one example, think back to a recent
argument you had with your teenage son. You remember your cogent reasons
well. Can you repeat his with equal accuracy? If you are a committed Republi-
can, you probably cannot describe the Democratic platform convincingly.

Scientists have known for over 200 years that expectations interfere with
accuracy. Research has shown that expectations lead you to see what you expect to see instead of the actual stimulus (just the way the FBI examiners "saw"
Mayfield's exemplar fingerprint matching the latent print from Spain). You make
mistakes in your tabulations in the direction of the outcome you expected. You
interpret your data to support your expectation when the data show something
different. Risinger et al. (2002), and more recently, Dror and Frazer-MacKensie
(2008), provide detailed reviews of the research evidence of expectation bias that
leads to inaccurate judgments during attention, perception, retention of memory,
retrieval of memory, and decision making. They focus on the full range of forensic identification procedures, including fingerprint comparisons. The National

Academy of Sciences Report (2009, sections 4-9,10,11) provides an overview of sources and kinds of cognitive bias. Expectations always influence decisions. They cannot be overcome by concentration, practice, or foresight.

Several different terms have been used for bias effects. We use the terms expectation and bias, which we treat as a mindset in cognitive processes. Bias distorts judgments and conclusions in predictable ways. When the biasing information is erroneous, the conclusions are more likely to be erroneous.

For these reasons, working scientists and companies attempting objective measurements go to extreme lengths to remove expectations, to keep their work and workers free from bias. To do this, the experimenter or tester who performs the testing is not allowed to know the status of the stimulus (the fingerprint examiner would not know whether the exemplar is an elimination or a suspect, or produced by AFIS or by police investigation), nor does he know the predicted outcome (the verifying examiner would not know the comparison and conclusion had already been made by someone else). *The only defense against being misled by irrelevant expectations is to prevent exposure to them.*

When a fingerprint examiner knows there's other evidence that the suspect is the perpetrator, that information biases him toward finding a match (Dror, Charlton and Peron, 2006). His expectation leads him to fill in missing information and resolve ambiguities in the latent in the direction of an identification (Office of the Inspector General, 2006). Without the expectation, the missing information would remain missing, and ambiguities in the features would remain uninterpreted.

9.2 Recent Fingerprint Experiments Demonstrating Bias

Three recent experiments by Dror and his colleagues demonstrate how these kinds of expectations can bias examiners' decisions during the course of fingerprint comparisons.

Dror, Peron, Hind, and Charlton (2005) gave *novice examiners* 96 pairs of fingerprints and asked them to judge whether the members of each pair were made by the same finger or by two different fingers. Forty-eight pairs were of good quality and relatively easy to compare (24 were from the same donor and 24 were from different donors). The other 48 pairs were of poor quality and quantity and lacked sufficient information to make a reliable identification. One-quarter of the 96 pairs were presented without biasing information, one-quarter were accompanied by a variety of unemotional illustrated stories about a non-violent crime, one-quarter were presented with an accompanying highly emotional story and pictures of a violent crime or severely injured victim, and the last one-quarter had the emotional story and pictures plus information implying the guilt of the suspect. The authors found that for the 48 relatively high quality pairs of fingerprints, there were no statistically significant differences in the number of identifications made as a function of the four expectation conditions. However, with the poor quality pairs, the more emotional the accompanying information, the more likely the subjects were to judge the pairs to match. Since the accompanying information was irrelevant to whether the pair of prints was made by the same donor, the main result shows that when examining difficult fingerprints, the irrelevant expectations created by the emotional information biased the novice examiners into making identifications.

We described the Dror, Charlton, and Peron (2006) experiment in Chapter 8, in which 4 of the 5 examiners changed their previous conclusion after being told biasing information. These results show that information influences examiners' comparison process so that, like the rest of us, they find what they expect to find.

The Dror and Charlton (2006) experiment was also reported in Chapter 8. It repeated Dror, Charlton, and Peron (2006) with more examiners, more pairs of fingerprints to compare again, and accompanying information biasing in both directions. The results followed the same pattern as in their previous experiment. For the easy/hard difference, one easy pair was changed and five hard pairs were changed. When a bias was given (24 comparisons), four conclusions (17 percent) were changed in the direction of the bias. Two changes were made without bias (8 percent). In total, six of the 48 comparisons (12.5 percent) were changed when the same examiner looked at them five years later. Most of the changes were made on the more difficult pairs to compare. The changes were not limited to a single, susceptible examiner. Four of the six examiners (two-thirds) made at least one change.

These results show that the erroneous identification by the FBI examiners in 2004 can be reproduced in the research laboratory. It is not a fluke. These results, in company with a wide body of research on cognitive psychology, mean that the presence of biasing information before and during fingerprint comparison leads to increased numbers of erroneous identifications.

Hall and Player (2008) published an attempted replication of Dror, Peron, Hind, and Charlton (2005) using *experienced* fingerprint examiners. No effect of bias was found. However, they manipulated the bias effect by accompanying statements that the crime was a forgery or a murder. This manipulation had succeeded with the inexperienced examiners in the Dror et al. (2005) experiment, but failed to affect these experienced examiners working in a police environment. In Dror's latter two experiments, using experienced examiners, much more powerful biases were created: the examiners were given information that directly confirmed or contradicted their former conclusions (e.g., the suspect was in jail at the time of the crime).

Langenburg et al. (2009) attempted to study bias effects during the verification stage of ACE. The results suggest that inconclusive judgments increase under biasing conditions. However, the results are uninterpretable because, according to the authors, when the participants in the study were debriefed, many in the biased groups revealed they had "caught on" to the intentions of the study. Several participants said they felt they were being given inappropriate information that "introduced the potential of some bias." Far from being biased, these subjects became suspicious and alert.

In the remainder of this chapter, we consider sources of bias in fingerprint crime laboratories. We focus on information flow, the ACE method, and automatic fingerprint searches.

9.3 Bias from Information Flow in Crime Laboratories

The pieces of physical evidence the fingerprint examiner needs in order to perform comparisons include a latent print, source information from the crime scene examination (photographs of the latent and of the surface on which it was found, and the purpose of the touch by the perpetrator), the lifting and processing procedures used, and an exemplar print. Any additional information biases the examiner and leads to a higher rate of error, as shown by Risinger et al. (2002) and the Dror experiments just reviewed.

Additional and irrelevant information comes in many different forms. In small crime laboratories, the examiner may be the same person who investigated the crime scene. If he is exposed to knowledge of the seriousness of the crime, other evidence incriminating this suspect, or reactions of other investigators who were also present, his judgment is influenced. Koppl (2005) reviews the practical difficulties and importance of separating crime laboratories administratively and functionally from police and sheriff departments. Similarly, the examiner should be unaware of whether the exemplar print came from a suspect or is an elimination print of someone lawfully present at the crime scene.

Knowledge of the importance of the case also biases the examiner (Dror et al., 2005). Analyses of the Mayfield erroneous identification (Stacey, 2004; Office of the Inspector General, 2006) attribute the knowledge held by all three FBI examiners that this was an international terrorist case, with lots of prestige on the line if the FBI could break it, as one source of the erroneous identification.

Challenge

In our experience, most crime laboratories are part of the police or sheriff department. Biasing discussion and rumors about every case are part of the everyday interaction in the work setting. The National Academy of Sciences Report (2009, section S-17, Recommendation 4) concludes: "To improve the scientific bases of forensic science examinations and to maximize independence from or autonomy within the law enforcement community, Congress should authorize and appropriate incentive funds to the National Institute of Forensic Science (NIFS) for allocation to state and local jurisdictions for the purpose of removing all public forensic laboratories and facilities from the administrative control of law enforcement agencies or prosecutors' offices."

A. Quality Control Manual Governing Information Flow

ASCLD (1998) recommends that an accredited crime laboratory have a quality control manual describing how work assignments are made, the permitted scope of information attached to fingerprint assignments, and what should *not* be given to examiners who might work on the case.

The National Academy of Sciences Report (2009, section S-18, Recommendation 5) concludes: "National Institute for Forensic Sciences should develop standard operating procedures (that will lay the foundation for model protocols) to minimize, to the greatest extent reasonably possible, potential bias and sources of human error in forensic practice."

Challenge

In our experience, most crime laboratories do not include information flow in their quality control regulations, or do not have a manual on quality control. Without quality control guidelines in place and enforced, the probability that examiners will be exposed to biasing information is greatly increased, thereby increasing for the laboratory output as a whole the probability of erroneous identifications.

9.4 Biases in the ACE Method

Each stage of the ACE method is open to bias when the steps are not followed properly, or in the correct order, or when the examiner has been exposed to biasing information.

A. Analysis Stage

1. Failure to conclude value/no value prior to seeing the exemplar

In step 1 of analysis, the examiner must decide whether the latent is of value before he sees the exemplar. Otherwise, he is more likely to judge an unusable latent to be of value, and carry out the comparison. Poor quality stimuli are more likely to result in erroneous identifications, as described in Chapter 2.

Challenge

Because examiners do not make bench notes, the prevalence of this biasing procedure is unknown.

2. Premature examination of the exemplar

The ACE method should stipulate that the examiner complete analysis of the latent print without looking at the exemplar print (Ashbaugh, 1999; Office of the Inspector General, 2006). Once the examiner is familiar with the exemplar, he "sees" characteristics in the latent that make it more consistent with the exemplar (Ashbaugh, 1999).

Challenge

Neither the IAI nor the ACE method requires examiners to complete analysis of the latent first. Many examiners testify that they begin analysis with the latent and exemplar side by side. This procedure is biased.

3. Incomplete analysis

In step 2 during analysis, the examiner labels every instance of a distortion. Bias arises if the examiner fails to describe these distortions before he sees the exemplar. The consequences of this omission occur during the comparison stage, if the examiner then finds a difference between the two prints. Now he cannot determine objectively whether the difference is due to a distortion that he had failed to notice during analysis, or to a two-donor pattern difference.

Challenge

Examiners are not required to keep bench notes of their analysis of a latent, so the prevalence of this bias is unknown.

4. Failure to select features to compare before seeing the exemplar

In step 4 of analysis, the examiner selects a set of features to use for the initial comparison. The features must be chosen before the examiner sees the exemplar. If an examiner uses the exemplar to choose the features to compare, he reads those features into the latent, a bias that makes an erroneous identification more likely.

Challenge

Examiners are not required to make bench notes, so the prevalence of this bias is unknown.

5. Failure to specify the location of each feature to be used for comparison

When features to be compared are described, they must also be located. If an examiner starts with the feature locations in the exemplar, he will accept a greater disagreement in location than if he started with locations in the latent. This bias makes erroneous identifications more likely.

Challenge

Examiners are not required to make bench notes, so the prevalence of this bias is unknown.

6. Failure to set a confidence level

In the fifth step of analysis, the examiner assigns the confidence he attaches to details in each area of the latent. If the examiner has failed to set confidence levels during analysis, bias created by the exemplar makes him more likely to accept a small difference as distortion when it should be the basis for exclusion.

Challenge

Examiners are not required to make bench notes, so the prevalence of this bias is unknown.

B. Comparison Stage

We describe four ways in which bias can influence an examiner's decisions during comparison.

1. Incomplete comparison of latent features

The examiner who curtails comparison because he expects an identification precludes the possibility of a two-donor pattern difference in the very next ridge. The expectation of identification makes an incomplete comparison more likely.

2. Re-analysis of a distorted feature

An examiner, comparing the latent and exemplar, finds a difference that is caused by a distortion he failed to note in the latent during analysis. If he uses the exemplar to define the latent ("I see a ridge ending in the exemplar, not in the latent, but powder or pressure must have filled it in"), he exposes himself to bias. He is now much more likely to fail to exclude when he should do so. Table 9.2 provides a dramatic example taken from the erroneous identification of Brandon Mayfield.

Table 9.2
The Erroneous Identification in the Mayfield Case

This illustrates the potential for error created by using information from the exemplar to analyze the latent. The examiner who initially analyzed the latent print from the crime scene labeled six features to encode the print for submission to an automated computer search. He labeled them from analysis of the latent alone. These are shown in the left column below. When Mayfield was erroneously identified as the donor of the latent, the same examiner used Mayfield's exemplar to review his analysis. Based on the exemplar, the examiner changed his interpretation of four of these features. His later descriptions are shown in the right column (taken from Office of the Inspector General, 2006).

#	Feature Encoded for IAFIS	Feature Identified in Mayfield Exemplar
2	Ending Ridge	Ending Ridge
3	Ending Ridge	Ending Ridge
4	Bifurcation	Ending Ridge
5	Bifurcation	Ending Ridge
12	Bifurcation	Ending Ridge
13	Ending Ridge	Bifurcation

In the Mayfield case, it is possible to compare this examiner's original, unbiased analysis, and his revised one based on knowledge of the exemplar, with the features in the exemplar from the known perpetrator. The examiner correctly specified 3 of the 6 features when he encoded them for IAFIS; he correctly specified only one after he revised his description based on the Mayfield exemplar (Office of the Inspector General, 2006). This documented example shows how the biasing effect of knowledge of the exemplar leads to error.

The Mayfield example also shows the importance of documenting, during the analysis stage, the confidence the examiner has placed in the type of feature identified. If the latent lacks sufficient quality to label features with certainty, use of an exemplar to specify those features creates a high probability of an erroneous match.

3. Reset confidence level

Suppose the examiner expressed strong certainty about some details in the latent during analysis. Now, looking at the exemplar during comparison, he sees that most, but not all of those features agree. For one that does not agree, he may rethink his earlier certainty: "I was sure this was a ridge ending, but now I realize the latent ridge was just a bit faint and actually continues." As soon as an examiner permits himself to describe the information in the latent based on seeing the exemplar, he is *creating* a match, not discovering a match. If he allows the exemplar to alter his unbiased judgment of the latent, he is likely to make an erroneous identification.

4. Teasing the points

If an examiner has not found enough agreement between the latent print and the exemplar print for an identification, he may be tempted to accept ambiguous characteristics to reach sufficiency. This very dangerous practice is called "teasing the points." Including ambiguous features multiplies the chances of an erroneous identification. The Office of the Inspector General (2006) noted this practice in the Mayfield case, and considered it one of the contributors to the erroneous identification.

C. Evaluation Stage

There are two ways bias affects the evaluation stage.

1. Reset agreement standards

During evaluation, the examiner determines the overall amount and quality of the agreement he noted in comparison. A collection of dubious agreements weighs toward an erroneous identification. Bias enters when weak agreements are re-evaluated upwards just because there are lots of them. Two wrongs do not make an identification more likely to be right.

2. Reset sufficiency standard

If an examiner expects an identification and lowers the amount of agreement he requires for an identification, an erroneous identification is more likely to occur.

Challenge

In the absence of an objective standard for how much agreement is needed for an identification, and how unambiguous each feature in agreement has to be, examiners have no way to know that they have changed the amount and quality of agreement they require.

Challenge

To date, the profession does not document through bench notes the steps of ACE when a comparison is performed. Potentially, every comparison brought into court has been biased in one or many ways.

D. Verification Stage

Bias enters verification of an ACE conclusion whenever verification is non-blind. The most serious bias is created by the second examiner anticipating a given outcome: "I expect to find an identification, because my colleague already found one. I do not expect to disagree, I know he's a very good examiner."

In Chapter 8 (see Table 8.1) we listed 22 erroneous identifications attested to in court. They were verified by 39 additional examiners. This suggests that asking another examiner to ratify the original conclusion is no guarantee that the conclusion is correct. Non-blind verification contributed to the Mayfield error (Office of the Inspector General, 2006).

E. Quality Control Manual for ACE Method

The ASCLD laboratory accreditation recommendations include a manual that describes and governs the use of the ACE method. This manual should contain a full description of the method, including verification, and protocols to avoid bias during the fingerprint comparison process.

Challenge

This manual has yet to be written. The Inspector General's report on the Mayfield case severely criticized the FBI for lacking such a manual. Without manuals describing the quality controls to prevent bias and procedures to enforce those regulations, bias remains unbridled.

9.5 Bias in AFIS Processing and Examination

When an examiner compares suspects produced by an AFIS search, he is exposed to five sources of bias in addition to those we described in the ACE method itself.

A. The Submission Process Requires the Examiner to Interpret the Latent

As we described in Chapter 6, many computer search systems require the technician to indicate the features or ridge paths on which to search. The prepared latent contains a number of decisions the technician made. Each decision interprets a detail in the latent, with unknown accuracy. The processed latent no longer matches the original latent, in that ambiguous features have been disambiguated.

Research results from a range of studies have shown that once you "know" the image, those details remain clear and you remain certain they are accurate (Haber and Hershenson, 1980). For these reasons, when the person who prepared the latent then applies ACE, even if he is now using the original latent to compare to the candidate exemplars, he "sees" the details he processed into the latent in order to submit it.

The outcome of this comparison is biased toward an identification in two ways. First, the examiner accepts as certain the features he interpreted as present. Second, the AFIS output is biased (by algorithm) to produce candidates that possess those features. Both biases increase the probability of an erroneous identification.

B. Failure to Analyze the Latent Print Before Comparison to AFIS Candidates

We described above the importance of complete analysis of the latent prior to seeing an exemplar. Failure to follow this procedure results in backward bias: features from the exemplar appear "distinct" in the latent. Using the exemplar to define the latent biases the results toward an erroneous identification. The AFIS technician who compares the incompletely analyzed latent to the AFIS exemplars is exposed to this bias. The fingerprint examiner who is given the latent and the exemplar from the AFIS search, and compares them side by side, without analyzing the latent first, is exposed to this bias.

C. Using the AFIS Rating to Choose Candidates to Compare

AFIS outputs include a ranking and/or rating of the amount of similarity between the submitted latent and each candidate. Ranking/rating information biases the examiner in three ways. He is more likely to compare higher ranked candidates first, even in the order of ranking; he is likely to devote more effort to them; and because examiners believe their identifications are "gold standard" and infallible, once an examiner makes an identification, he does not compare the remaining candidates. Each of these increases the chances of an erroneous identification.

D. Knowledge of Extraneous Information When Making an Identification

Just as biasing information about a suspect can lead to an erroneous identification during ACE, it can infiltrate the comparison process based on an AFIS output. The examiner must carry out the comparison without knowledge of the seriousness of the crime and other incriminating information about the AFIS candidates.

E. Reconfiguring an Input to AFIS

The majority of AFIS searches do not produce a hit. Some diligent examiners try again. To do so, they alter the details they had submitted to the search system the first time. This increases the probability of an erroneous identification. A second strategy is to submit the latent to a different database. The National Academy of Sciences Report (2009, section 10-4) asserts: "In fact, experienced latent print examiners have found that different systems will retrieve different prints in response to a given input map of features, and they have learned system-specific ways of annotating features on a latent print in order to maximize the success of each system's (inferred) search algorithms." In other words, the examiner adjusts his interpretation to the system.

An AFIS failure to produce a match arises for three reasons. The most likely is that the perpetrator is not in the database. A second possibility is that the AFIS algorithms are not powerful enough to find the true exemplar in the database. For either reason, the AFIS output is the most useful the examiner can get, and further attempts can only produce error.

A third possibility is that the examiner mislabeled characteristics of the latent when he encoded it for submission. If this happened, isn't this diligent examiner more likely to get the features right the second time? The answer is, No. When he altered the details of the latent print to repeat the search, he increased the probability of finding a set of erroneous candidates, because he used less likely features to input. If the examiner alters the input enough times, eventually he'll get a candidate with sufficiently similar characteristics for an identification. The probability of a correct match decreases with each reconfiguration of the latent.

F. Biases Associated with Cold Hits

We reviewed in Chapter 6 the statistical evidence that the probability of a correct identification is very tiny when the only evidence implicating the suspect is a cold hit from an AFIS search. Failure by the police and the court to consider this statistical evidence biases their estimate of the accuracy of cold hits substantially.

A cold hit itself produces a bias. When the police now attempt to find other evidence to link the cold suspect to the crime, they believe they have the right suspect. As the research discussed at the beginning of this chapter shows, people find what they expect to find. Any circumstantial link between the cold hit suspect and the crime becomes "confirmed evidence," and disconfirming evidence is likely to be ignored. This greatly increases the chances of an erroneous outcome.

Challenge
No studies have been published to show the magnitude of erroneous identifications that occur as a result of these sources of bias with the use of automated search systems,

Challenge
We have never seen a manual introduced in court that includes procedures to prevent bias when AFIS searches are involved.

The FBI's erroneous identification does not reflect badly on the FBI's examiners. Their examiners are humans, and their cognitive processes are subject to bias. The Brandon Mayfield error spotlights the need for quality control measures that prevent examiner exposure to the kinds of information that produce bias.

Challenge
Cognitive scientists already know a great deal about the increased probability of erroneous conclusions when judgments are biased. The fingerprint profession has yet to mandate quality control procedures that eliminate the sources of bias described in this chapter.

Chapter 10

Standards Governing the Qualifications of Fingerprint Examiners and Crime Laboratories

Your family doctor has identified your illness as heliosophocobra, a very serious disease, and has suggested a specific course of treatment. You want a second opinion about the diagnosis and treatment from another expert. What standards do you apply to choose this important specialist?

You might think about the quality of his training. Did he attend a well-known medical school? You of course require that this specialist passed his medical boards. You would probably want evidence that he has extensive experience with your disease. You might value his reputation, his prominence in his field, or his attendance at relevant seminars. You would also evaluate the reputation of the hospital where he works.

When a fingerprint examiner testifies to an identification in court, he does so as an expert with expert qualifications. In this chapter, we focus on the regulations that govern the qualifications of fingerprint examiners and the crime laboratories in which they perform their work.

10.1 Fingerprint Examiners and Crime Laboratories

In the United States, five professional organizations represent or have some regulatory power over the qualifications of fingerprint examiners and the standards and requirements to be met by crime laboratories performing fingerprint tasks. These organizations (described in Table 1.1) include the IAI, SWGFAST, US-DOJ, ASCLD, and the FBI. Only a few individual states, such as Illinois, exercise more stringent requirements than the organizations just listed.

Nearly 5,000 of the 7,000 members of the IAI list themselves as latent fingerprint examiners in the IAI directory. There is no requirement that practicing examiners belong to the IAI, and some IAI-listed examiners perform tasks other than latent-to-exemplar comparison. The actual number of practicing latent print examiners is unknown.

The number of crime laboratories is also unknown. Of the 350 crime laboratory directors who are members of ASCLD, 315 represent laboratories that are accredited by ASCLD or Forensic Quality Services (Fitzpatrick, 2008). According to Fitzpatrick, these two organizations are the two accrediting bodies for laboratories employing fingerprint examiners. However, Fitzpatrick estimates that in the United States, the number of police, sheriffs' departments, and private laboratories providing forensic services of latent fingerprint analysis may be as high as 8,000, the majority of which are unaccredited and not subjected to regulations promulgated by fingerprint organizations. ASCLD (2004) carried out a study in which it reported that two-thirds of fingerprint identifications occur outside traditional crime laboratories. Fitzpatrick lists some of the quality controls that would be instantiated if these laboratories received accreditation.

We consider standards pertaining to fingerprint examiners first, and then standards for quality control that govern the crime laboratories in which they work.

10.2 Standards Regulating Fingerprint Examiners

Standards governing the qualifications for fingerprint examiners pertain to pre-employment education, initial training, subsequent supervised training, work experience, certification, demonstrated proficiency in the performance of their jobs, and court testimony.

Your doctor, and the specialist to whom you turn for a second opinion, received a Bachelor's Degree that included a number of required courses, such as biology and physiology. Both doctor and specialist then attended four years of medical school, during which a series of courses was required. Medical doctors-to-be next are required to have a specified period of general supervised training and experience, an internship, followed by a specified period of supervised training and experience in their specialty, a residency. Then every would-be doctor must pass a nationally administered certification test, medical boards. Only then does a trainee qualify as a medical doctor. Only then is he permitted to practice independently.

A. Regulatory Standards for Latent Print Examiner (LPE) Pre-Professional Education and Prior Experience

With the exception of the FBI, none of the other organizations listed above requires a specific kind or amount of education and prior experience to begin training as a latent print examiner.

Starting in 2005, SWGFAST recommended a B.A. degree as a minimum qualification for a person entering latent print comparison training. However, the IAI does not publish the degrees held by its members, and there is no way to determine the extent to which this recommendation has been followed.

ASCLD recommends, as an "important" qualification (75 percent attainment), that for a laboratory to receive and maintain accreditation by the ASCLD, every latent print examiner have a B.A. degree. However, ASCLD does not publish information regarding the number of examiners working in accredited crime laboratories who have B.A. degrees, and because this is a recommendation and not a requirement for accreditation, it is not enforced. ASCLD does not specify any desirable or minimum educational requirement for the estimated 85 percent of laboratories that are not accredited.

A few crime laboratories have their own entrance level requirements of prior work experience, or amount and/or kind of education completed. The FBI is the most stringent, now requiring an entering trainee to have received a B.A. in or related to the physical sciences.

Just as there is no standardized amount of prior education and experience requirements to enter training in the fingerprint profession, there is no specified prior coursework (National Academy of Sciences Report (2009, section 2-4)). There are no prerequisites comparable to the medical student's required training in biology and physiology before he enters medical school (Grieve, 1996).

The majority of fingerprint examiners are former sworn police officers who transferred into the crime laboratory (National Academy of Sciences Report, 2009). They brought with them whatever education requirements they had to meet to become and remain police officers. A relatively small but growing number of new trainees are college graduates. Fingerprint trainees and examiners in virtually every crime laboratory have a diverse mix of backgrounds and education.

Challenge

The SWGFAST recommendation that trainees have a B.A. degree, particular experiences, or particular coursework is not a requirement and the amount of compliance has not been documented. Our experience in reviewing the résumés of fingerprint examiners is that most do not meet the minimum recommended requirements.

B. Regulatory Standards for LPE Initial Training

Medical doctor trainees attend four years of medical school following their undergraduate training. Much of the content of their coursework is standardized across medical schools throughout the country.

In contrast, with the exception of the FBI, none of the other organizations listed above requires a standardized training protocol. The vast majority of training that working examiners receive occurs on-the-job in the crime laboratory where they are first employed. Some agencies send new examiners to a one- or two-week course. Few crime laboratories have a formalized curriculum for training new employees, nor are there formalized requirements for periodic testing of the acquisition of new skills from the training (National Academy of Sciences Report, 2009, section 5-8) .

The FBI's training program is the most extensive in the profession (described in detail in Plaza II Daubert hearing by Meagher, 2002). The FBI now requires a two-year training program that includes latent print development techniques, formal classroom instruction on fingerprint classification, examination methodology (ACE), practical exercises, and skills assessment testing, case examination procedures and protocols, mentoring, oral board examinations, mock court exercises, and a final certification examination that tests both fingerprint background knowledge and fingerprint comparisons.

In a recent Strategic Plan, ASCLD (2006) identified standardized training as a high priority need. However, even if the ASCLD standards were mandatory and included uniform training, those training protocols would be required only in crime laboratories that meet and maintain the ASCLD accreditation standards. Eighty-five percent of the laboratories in the U.S. would not be obligated to employ those training materials.

C. Regulatory Standards for LPE Training to Competence

Medical doctors pass a national test in order to demonstrate mastery of their training. In contrast, there are no standardized tests required of a fingerprint examiner to demonstrate he is properly trained.

In theory, two approaches could provide evidence of trained-to-competency. The first would be the kind of standardized training program just described for the FBI, with proficiency tests at each step designed to show the trainee has mastered that material. The second would be a nationally administered "licensing" test, equivalent to the medical boards taken by doctors. Neither approach has been incorporated by the fingerprint profession.

SWGFAST (2002b) issued a set of recommendations on "Training to Competence for Latent Print Examiners." The recommendations state that knowledge of required objectives must be evidenced by passing written examinations and practical exercises, and by communicating an understanding of the underlying principles. However, the SWGFAST (2002b) recommendations do not describe how this knowledge should be trained, who should provide the training, or how training should be tested. The SWGFAST objectives are recommendations only, not requirements. In current practice in most crime laboratories, an examiner trainee is deemed competent to work independently when his immediate supervisor so decides.

Challenge

The fingerprint profession has neither standardized training protocols nor standardized proficiency testing during or upon completion of training. This means that individual examiners cannot document either the quality of their training or their mastery of it. Successful completion of coursework, even when tests are included, does not provide such evidence.

Challenge

With the exception of examiners who have gone through the FBI's training program or been trained in the few other crime laboratories with formal training programs, the majority of fingerprint examiners have received and continue to receive most of their training on-the-job. The level of training, the method(s) taught, the closeness of supervision, and testing to demonstrate acquisition of knowledge and skill are haphazard and unregulated.

D. Regulatory Standards for LPE Supervised Experience

Medical doctors undergo mandatory supervised experience during internship and residency lasting a number of years. In contrast, the fingerprint profession does not specify the amount of supervised experience an examiner needs before he can work independently. Typically, the kind and extent of supervision of an examiner trained on-the-job is determined by the individual laboratory or by the individual doing the supervision.

Challenge

The absence of uniform supervised training, like the absence of a uniform training protocol, means that different examiners receive different training, and individual examiners differ greatly in their skill when they begin to work on their own.

E. Regulatory Standards for LPE Continuing Education

Many professions, including specialized disciplines in medicine such as psychiatry, require certified, experienced practitioners to participate periodically in a specified amount of relevant coursework to maintain their certification. The fingerprint profession has no such requirement. The IAI offers a range of continuing education courses including fingerprint classification, processing, crime scene collection, and fingerprint comparison methods, from a day to a week in length. These are open to anyone who pays the tuition. The FBI also teaches a number of such courses for its specialists, and until recently allowed other fingerprint examiners to enroll. ASCLD (2006) recommends that fingerprint examiners complete seminars and training courses in their specialty on a regular basis. Many laboratories do not enforce this recommendation.

Challenge

The absence of a requirement for practicing fingerprint examiners to keep current in their field severely limits their exposure to new skills, upgraded technology, and recent advances. Most examiners whose résumés we have read have taken few such courses.

F. Regulatory Standards for LPE Latent Comparison Experience

Examiners who attest to an identification in court frequently present their years of experience as evidence of their accuracy. Because examiners do not have access to ground truth in their casework, they do not know if they are getting better with their experience, or merely repeating the same skills (and the same mistakes) over and over again. Improvement as a function of experience could be shown by improvement in proficiency test scores in which ground truth is known.

Challenge

The absence of standardized, graded proficiency tests means that examiners cannot document their improvement with experience. The profession has not offered data, such as correlations between years of work and supervisor ratings, as evidence of improvement with experience. The only standard the profession has to measure experience is years on the job.

G. Regulatory Standards for LPE Proficiency Testing

Proficiency concerns the quality and quantity of work produced by each employee individually, and by an organization as a whole. Medical doctors are required to undergo continued proficiency testing in the form of periodically retaking their board examinations. Airplane pilots, truck drivers, and a range of other skilled practitioners are subject to similar requirements. Fingerprint examiners are not.

The SWGFAST (2004) and the ASCLD (1998) have made recommendations, subsequently adopted by the IAI, as to the frequency, content and administration of proficiency tests for fingerprint examiners. However, these recommendations are neither enforced nor enforceable, and the majority of working fingerprint examiners do not take the offered proficiency tests.

Challenge

These recommendations do not include required standards for proficiency testing. See Chapter 7 for a detailed discussion of the kinds of standards needed, such as which skills to assess and at what level of difficulty.

H. Regulatory Standards for LPE Certification

Whereas all medical doctors with an M.D. degree and experts in many other fields are required to pass a nationally administered certification test, no comparable test is required for fingerprint examiners.

The current pass rate for the certification test, since 2005, is about 70 percent (IAI Certification Board, 2009) a substantial increase from the 50 percent pass rate for the prior 30 years. Two changes have occurred with respect to the test. The time limits to complete the test have been extended, and in the past several years, the IAI has offered courses specifically designed to help examiners pass the test. Both practices should improve test scores.

Challenge

As described in Chapter 7, the IAI certification test is highly flawed. The difficulty level of the individual items is not controlled, there is no evidence of the validity and reliability of the test, it is not representative of normal casework, and it is not administered in a way that generalizes to casework. These failures mean that the certification test as given cannot be used as evidence of a level of excellence of the examiners taking the test.

Challenge

The majority of working fingerprint examiners has never applied for certification. As noted in Chapter 7, only working examiners with substantial training and experience can apply to take the test.

Challenge

Of the 5,000 IAI-listed fingerprint examiners working in this country, only 761 (15 percent) are certified by the IAI (2009). This already small number is dropping due to retirements and deaths of previously certified members who are not being replaced by new certifications. The net loss in 2008 alone was 10 percent (Latent Print Certification Board, 2009). An unknown number of practicing examiners are not members of the IAI, so the actual percent certified is lower.

I. Regulatory Standards for LPE Court Testimony

None of the five organizations that could require or recommend qualifications for a fingerprint examiner to testify as an expert in court has done so. Anyone who claims to have training and experience as a fingerprint examiner can offer himself as an expert to the court. The individual court, and not the profession, determines whether he is qualified to offer testimony on a fingerprint comparison.

Challenge

In the absence of qualification requirements specified by the profession, examiners who testify in court range widely in their expertise, and, to an unknown extent, in their accuracy.

Challenge

Examiners who testify in court justify their expertise and their accuracy on the basis of their *training* and their *experience*, neither of which is defined and quantitatively measured.

Challenge

The National Academy of Sciences Report (2009, section S-19, Recommendation 7) enjoins: "No person (public or private) should be allowed to practice in a forensic science discipline or testify as a forensic science professional without certification. Certification requirements should include, at a minimum, written examinations, supervised practice, proficiency testing, continuing education, recertification procedures, adherence to a code of ethics, and effective disciplinary procedures."

Challenge

We have reviewed the standards for the qualifications of individual examiners based on their background, training, employment, work experience, certifications, and acceptance by courts. The standards are either absent or in the form of un-enforced and un-monitored recommendations.

10.3 Standard Operating Procedures in Crime Laboratories

The hospital in which your doctor and specialist work hires only qualified medical personnel, those who meet the specifications of the American Medical Association. The hospital also conforms to standard operating procedures that regulate the work these personnel perform. Comparable SOPs for a crime laboratory include, for example, the work flow within the laboratory, regulations for how a fingerprint comparison is performed, verification procedures, the contents of bench notes and case reports, procedures for supervision and for case reviews, and the investigation of errors.

A. SOPs for Laboratory Work Flow

Laboratory SOPs for work flow serve to assure uniform quality of the laboratory's work product and to reduce the chances of the kinds of bias discussed in Chapter 9. The IAI, SWGFAST and ASCLD have not made recommendations to address the bias issues raised in Chapter 9.

Challenge

Many laboratories have no quality control manuals. We have never seen a manual that included measures to prevent bias. The work flow is largely unregulated and the importance of preventing bias has been largely unrecognized by the profession.

B. SOPs for Fingerprint Comparisons

The laboratory's fingerprint comparison manual describes the method to be used and the standard procedures to be followed when comparing fingerprints. Specification of the comparison process permits the laboratory to regulate and evaluate examiner performance, and the Court to evaluate whether those procedures were followed in the instant case.

Challenge

We have never seen a crime laboratory manual that contained a detailed SOP for fingerprint examinations. The Office of the Inspector General's (2006) negative assessment of the FBI's laboratory manual was highly critical of the absence of a fully specified procedure for fingerprint comparison. The examiners' comparison processes are unregulated by the laboratories employing examiners.

C. SOPs for Verification

The IAI, SWGFAST, and the ASCLD recommend (but do not require) that every identification be verified before the report on the case is released to the requesting agency. They also recommend that the verification be arranged by the laboratory supervisor; the verification should be done by an examiner of equal or more senior status to the identifier; and the verification should be a completely independent examination of the latent and exemplar prints. Verification SOPs would specify how the repeated comparison is to be performed.

Challenge

Explicit SOPs for verification are not published in crime laboratory protocols. Crime laboratories rarely follow the substance of the IAI and ASCLD recommendations regarding independent verification. The Office of the Inspector General (2006) noted the failure in the FBI laboratory to perform independent verifications.

D. SOPs for Bench Notes and Casework Reports

One method to assess the quality of an examiner's performance is to evaluate his bench notes and his subsequent case report. Bench notes serve several additional, critical functions. They document the specific features in the latent print that the examiner used to reach his conclusion, and the steps he followed during the comparison process.

The IAI, SWGFAST, and ASCLD have recommended requirements for reports. In Chapter 5 we described a report form created by Ashbaugh (2005b), which is based on bench notes, and is used routinely by the Royal Canadian Mounted Police. This format serves to document the major components of the

ACE in the instant case, it suffices for internal quality control analyses, and would support the examiner's testimony in court.

The Office of the Inspector General (2006) repeatedly noted the omission of bench notes in its analysis of the FBI erroneous identification of Mayfield. A New Hampshire court ruled in a specific case (*New Hampshire v. Langill*, 2007) that without bench notes, the court would not accept the evidence of fingerprint comparisons. (This ruling was reversed (*New Hampshire v. Langill*, 2008) on technical grounds.)

Challenge

At present, bench notes are rarely required and rarely made. Typical case reports contain only the examiner's conclusion.

E. SOPs for Supervision and Case Reviews

ASCLD recommends that periodic, scheduled reviews of completed case reports from each examiner be made by the supervisor, who then provides an oral report to the examiner and a written report of the evaluation, ideally on a prepared form, which goes into the personnel file.

Challenge

SOPs governing supervision of the work of individual examiners are rarely in place. This means that the accuracy of laboratories' work product is not uniformly evaluated.

F. SOPs to Monitor and Investigate Errors

A quality control manual should describe SOPs for the laboratory's error detection procedures, and resolutions and responses whenever a verifier disagrees with the conclusion of the original examiner. These SOPs serve to identify the reasons why a disagreement or error occurred. Based on the findings, the laboratory can put into place new procedures to reduce the chances of a similar error occurring again.

Challenge

Published SOPs on error detection, analysis, and modification to prevent further similar errors are rare. The profession is highly secretive about the occurrence of errors. Publicizing errors permits analysis of their causes and prevents future similar errors.

The National Academy of Sciences Report (2009, section 7-19, recommendation 8) advises: "Forensic laboratories should establish routine quality assurance and quality control procedures to ensure the accuracy of forensic analyses and the work of forensic practitioners. Quality control procedures should be designed to identify mistakes, fraud, and bias; confirm the continued validity and reliability of standard operating procedures and protocols; ensure that the best practices are being followed; and correct procedures and protocols that are found to need improvement."

Challenge

The training and proficiency of expert witnesses such as medical doctors are strictly regulated. The exception is the fingerprint examiner.

Explicit quality controls govern the operation of workplaces of medical doctors in the form of detailed manuals that regulate work flow, work procedures and evaluation of work product. The exception is the crime laboratory.

Chapter 11

Challenges to Claims by the Fingerprint Profession About Fingerprint Comparison Accuracy

The challenges to fingerprints we have raised rest entirely upon scientific issues and can be answered with empirical studies. When defense attorneys have challenged the admissibility of fingerprint evidence in court, based upon the absence of scientific evidence to support the validity of the comparison method, the government has responded with a combination of empirically untrue and rhetorical claims. We review these here.

11.1 Empirical Claims
A. Examiners Employ a Single Comparison Method Known as ACE

The FBI claims in Daubert hearings (Meagher, 1999) that all examiners now use the ACE method when comparing fingerprints, and that there are no other methods in use by fingerprint examiners today. Ashbaugh (2005c) makes a similar claim. Practicing examiners almost uniformly refer to the fingerprint comparison method they employ as ACE. However, as we showed in Chapter 5, there is no single ACE method. No complete description exists in the literature, published descriptions differ in fundamental ways, and the profession has not adopted and approved a specific description of the method. Further, there is no standardized training program, so that different examiners receive different training. Current proficiency tests, such as CTS, do not require examiners to record the steps they use to reach a conclusion, nor are examiners required to make bench notes on the job during the comparison process itself. Consequently, there is no evidence available as to what method the examiner actually applied during any single comparison. There is no evidentiary basis for the government claim that examiners use a single method.

B. The ACE Error Rate is (Close to) Zero, Because Few Publicized Erroneous Identifications Have Been Found

Meagher (2002) reported that in his 35 years working for the FBI, he had never seen or heard of an erroneous identification made by an FBI agent. Since such an error would be widely publicized, a lack of publicity can assure the court that no such errors had occurred. The wide news coverage of the subsequent May-field erroneous identification shows that Meagher was right about the publicity. However, as we pointed out in Chapter 8, discovery of the error in the Mayfield case depended upon an extremely rare fluke: two independent crime laboratories performed the same latent-exemplar comparisons.

In another federal court (*U.S. v. Baines*, 2007), Meagher reported that the FBI has averaged one erroneous identification every 11 years. He noted that since the FBI makes about 1 million identifications every year, the erroneous identification rate for the FBI is about one for every 11 million identifications (p. 99). We classify this argument as rhetorical because neither Meagher nor anyone else has produced data to support any of these numbers.

With respect to the number of *erroneous identifications* made, Meagher claimed in 2002 that the FBI had never in its 60-year history made an erroneous identification (*U.S. v. Plaza*); two years later he admitted that the Mayfield identification was erroneous (the first one in over 60 years); and three years later he asserted the error rate is one erroneous identification every 11 years (presumably now five others have come to Mr. Meagher's notice, though he did not identify them). No crime laboratory, including the FBI, has reported the number of erroneous identifications it makes and discovers in-house. The number of erroneous identifications attested to in court, by FBI or other examiners, is unknown, as we discussed in Chapter 8.

Many combined factors make this number unknowable. Ground truth is not known in casework, so the examiner's assertion of an identification does not make it necessarily true. Also, the error rate of the ACE method itself is unknown, but, as we showed in Chapter 5, the subjective judgments that pervade ACE introduces likelihood of error. Empirical evidence, as we presented in Chapter 8, shows that examiners disagree about the same print at every step in ACE, indicating that the method is unreliable and has poor validity. However, the actual amount of error introduced by the method, independent of examiner error, is unknown. Examiner proficiency cannot be assessed, as we discussed in Chapter 7, so the contribution of examiner error to the erroneous identification rate is unknown. Independent review and verification of FBI casework does not normally occur (one of the very rare exceptions was the Mayfield case: that error was not found by examiners working within the FBI, but by examiners in an independent laboratory in another country). The legal system itself makes it extremely difficult for a convicted person to demonstrate innocence (Scheck et al., 2001). Verifications are not always performed, and when done, are rarely performed blind. Most fingerprint identifications are not challenged in court, either because the defendant pled to some other charge, or because the defense did not obtain a second opinion. Meagher's estimate of the number of erroneous identifications made by FBI examiners has no empirical foundation.

With respect to the number of *identifications* made, Meagher reported in *U.S. v. Baines* (2007) that the FBI makes 1 million fingerprint identifications each year. No available information supports this number. No crime laboratory, including the FBI laboratory, has reported the number of fingerprint cases they process, or the number of conclusions of identification they make. One million identifications per year translates into more than 4,000 identifications per working day. During the time period referred to by Meagher, the FBI employed approximately 60 fingerprint examiners doing casework (Meagher, 2002), which would translate into over eight identifications per examiner per day, or more than one identification per examiner per hour. In the same federal court, Meagher testified that identifications are rarely made, and that most positive conclusions are exclusions. In Chapter 8, we estimated that no more than one identification is made for each 100 latent prints found and examined. If Meagher's numbers were accurate and the laboratory's output were more than 4,000 identifications per day, each FBI examiner would have to work on hundreds of fingerprint cases per day. In our experience, examiners do not complete a fraction of such a figure.

Neither Meagher nor anyone else has produced data to support these numbers. Meagher's estimate of the number of identifications made by FBI examiners has no empirical foundation, and appear to be massively inflated.

Meagher's claim referred to the FBI. The data in Table 8.1, in which a total of 61 examiners made or verified erroneous identifications in court, show that these errors are being made in other crime laboratories and do reach court. Discovery of these errors, as in the Mayfield case, depended upon unlikely chance.

C. Proficiency Test Results Indicate a Very Low ACE Error Rate

The fingerprint profession has referred to results from proficiency tests as evidence of low error rates of the ACE method (Cole, 2005). As we described in Chapter 7, because the proficiency tests do not reflect casework and have not been validated, they cannot be used as evidence of examiner accuracy—or inaccuracy.

More importantly, because none of the published tests in use requires the examiner to document the method he used to reach his conclusions, the results of these tests cannot be used as evidence for the validity (accuracy) of ACE.

D. ACE is Based on the Scientific Method

Several prominent examiners (Ashbaugh, 1999; Triplett and Cooney, 2006; K. Wertheim, 2003) have argued that because ACE involves hypothesis testing by an examiner, which is a component of the scientific method, the ACE method itself is valid. This claim is incorrect. One possibility is that the examiner does not begin with a hypothesis, but applies ACE to determine *whether* the prints do or do not match. In this case, he presumably would not claim he was hypothesis testing. Alternatively, an examiner can begin a fingerprint comparison using one of two hypotheses: the predicted outcome is identification, or exclusion. In either case, the hypothesis refers to the outcome of a single case being "tested" by an application of the ACE method. The accuracy of the hypothesis is not being tested, because in casework the correct answer is unknown. Further, the outcome of the particular case is not a test of the accuracy of the ACE method itself. To test that, the scientific method is applied to determine whether the application of ACE produces correct conclusions. To test this hypothesis, a large number of fingerprint pairs are needed, with ground truth known for each one, and a large number of highly skilled examiners are needed who demonstrate that they have followed the official description of the ACE method (we described this experiment in detail in Chapter 8). This is an entirely different set of procedures from comparing a single pair of fingerprints and offering a conclusion without knowledge of ground truth.

The argument that applying the ACE method to a single fingerprint comparison has its roots in the scientific method of hypothesis testing is erroneous. The results of a single comparison do not provide information about the accuracy of the method itself.

E. Examiner Certainty Makes Conclusions Valid

Fingerprint examiners claim that the error rate of the ACE method is zero, because they only testify to a conclusion when they feel absolutely certain they are right. However, scientific research has repeatedly shown that certainty is not a measure of correctness, and that the correlation between certainty and accuracy is very low under normal circumstances (Wells et al., 2007).

F. The 50K Study Demonstrates that Fingerprints are Unique

We described this study in Chapter 2 and again in Chapter 8. Government witnesses sometimes assert that the results of the first part of the 50K study prove that fingerprints are unique. Underlying this claim is the unspoken assumption that if fingerprints are unique, they can be matched correctly to an exemplar from the true donor. In a trivial sense irrelevant to fingerprint comparison, it is true that every fingerprint, whether latent or exemplar, is unique, that is, no two *different* prints from the same finger are ever identical. In contrast, it's trivial and obvious that if I make a fingerprint and then make a photographic or digital copy of that image, the pattern in the two copies will be identical. This is exactly what was done in the 50K study, and the computer successfully found great similarity between the identical copies and less similarity between non-identical prints. The 50K study as performed fails to demonstrate the uniqueness of exemplars. It also fails altogether to demonstrate that human fingerprint examiners can distinguish correctly between two different images from single and multiple donors.

G. The 50K Study Demonstrates that Latent Prints are Correctly Matched to Exemplars

Government witnesses sometimes assert that the results of the second part of the 50K study prove that latent fingerprints can be matched to the correct exemplar with astronomical accuracy. This claim is wrong, because the second part of the 50K study did not use latent prints. A latent print is always a different take from the exemplar and often contains far less pattern information. The so-called latents in the 50K study were created by masking off all but the information-rich central 21.7 percent of the exemplar, and comparing it to the unmasked copy of itself. The results do not apply to latents or to fingerprint comparison accuracy.

11.2 Rhetorical Claims
A. One Hundred Years of Court Acceptance Mean the ACE Method is Valid

Many government witnesses (that is, fingerprint examiners) have testified that the validity of the ACE method has been tested by its continued acceptance throughout 100 years of history (e.g., Meagher, 2002). No one has claimed that the ACE method, as distinct from fingerprint evidence, has been accepted for 100 years. Even if this claim were made, the hundred years of acceptance would provide only a face validity that argues that fingerprint individuations must be accurate because people have believed them for a long time. Face validity is not a scientific test of accuracy, only of belief. Validity can only be tested by an empirical experiment, such as we described in Chapter 8.

B. Adversarial Testing Shows the Error Rate of ACE is Zero

Government witnesses in some Daubert hearings have argued that the results of application of the ACE method are tested through the adversarial process during each trial itself (e.g., *U.S. v. Havvard*, 2001). Since it is claimed in these hearings that no erroneous individuations have ever been uncovered during direct and cross examination, this procedure of testing shows the error rate of the method is zero.

Adversarial testing does not provide a mechanism to assess the error rate of ACE. The vast majority of cases involving fingerprint evidence result in plea bargains, or the fingerprint evidence goes unchallenged and therefore never is subjected to the adversarial process or to a second opinion. Far more importantly, ground truth is unknown during adversarial proceedings, just as it is during casework, so the outcome of the court proceedings cannot be used to assess validity of the method used.

C. Verification Assures the Error Rate of ACE is Close to Zero

Some government witnesses have argued that verification procedures guarantee that errors do not occur, because a second examiner checks the conclusion of the first (*U.S. v. Havvard*, 2001).

Not all laboratories require verification. Those that do rarely require blind verification. Non-blind verification permits bias to reduce the chances of detecting errors, as we described in Chapter 9.

Crime laboratories closely guard and do not publish results on the number of verifications they do, the number of those that produced different conclusions, and how those differences were resolved. The extent to which errors are reduced by current practice is simply unknown.

D. Verification Procedures Provide a Test of the Validity of ACE

Some government witnesses have argued that verification procedures represent a testing of the method, since a second examiner checks the conclusion of the first (*U.S. v. Havvard*, 2001). Verification testing fails in several ways to provide evidence of validity. In casework verification testing, ground truth is unknown, and agreement between two examiners might mean that they both were correct in the identification, or that they both made an error either by chance or because some property of the method led both to make the same error.

E. Second Opinions Protect an Innocent Defendant

The government has suggested that a defendant can always request a second opinion, so an erroneous conclusion would be found. In Chapter 8 we reviewed evidence that shows that two examiners comparing the same set of fingerprints do not always agree on their conclusions. How good are second opinions of contested evidence?

In the absence of scientific evidence of an error rate of the ACE method and the error rate of examiners revealed by valid proficiency testing programs, no confidence accrues from a second opinion. As we discuss in Chapter 12, a second opinion is no substitute for a challenge of the scientific status of the method and/or the examiner.

F. The Error Rate of the ACE Method is Zero

Cole (2005) quotes several prominent latent print examiners who have made this assertion, including Meagher (Trial Transcript at 154-56, *U.S. v. Mitchell*, Cr. No. 96-407 (E.D. Pa. July 8, 1999) and K. Wertheim (2001) and Grieve (2001), who wrote: "...if the methodology of ACE-V (analysis, comparison, evaluation and verification) is properly applied during an [sic] latent print examination, the error rate will be zero."

These examiners also assert that when errors do occur, they are the result of practitioner error. When all errors are attributed to the practitioner, then by tautology the method is error free. This is not a scientific statement. It is an untestable circular claim.

G. Only Poorly Trained or Inexperienced Examiners Make Erroneous Identifications

The fingerprint profession has claimed that erroneous identifications are only made by poorly trained or inexperienced practitioners. When the method is used by well-trained and experienced examiners, no errors are ever made (Meagher, 2002; 2003).

A number of scientists have noted that if the cause of errors is attributed to practitioners because of their inadequate training and experience, examiner training and experience need to be standardized and tested, and the results of those tests must be known for each examiner *before* an error occurs. Otherwise, this reasoning is circular (Cole, 2007).

This claim is also contrary to fact. The three FBI examiners who concurred in the misidentification of the Madrid bomber (Stacey, 2004) were among the most senior, most experienced, and most trained in the profession.

We pointed out in Chapters 7 and 8 that the absence of objective measures of the amount of information present in latent prints, combined with the absence of a specified ACE methodology, preclude separation of method and practitioner error. Neither the accuracy of the method nor the accuracy of the individual examiner can be tested at present.

Chapter 12

Challenges to Fingerprints

In this chapter we summarize the scientific challenges we have raised to the fingerprint profession and to the comparison method, ACE. We group them into challenges based on the inadequate professional requirements for latent print examiners; lack of quality controls for the laboratories in which examiners work; and absence of empirical, scientific evidence to support the comparisons examiners perform and the conclusions they reach. We conclude with a summary of recent court decisions in which challenges to the admissibility of fingerprint evidence have prevailed.

12.1 Challenges Based on Inadequate Professional Requirements for Latent Print Examiners

The first set of challenges focuses on the selection, training, experience, proficiency, certification and court testimony standards that apply to fingerprint examiners. These were discussed in Chapters 7 and 10.

A. Selection

The SWGFAST recommendations that beginning trainees have a B.A. degree, particular background experience, and relevant coursework are not requirements. The amount of compliance has not been documented. Under current conditions, these data cannot be collected. Our experience in reviewing the résumés of fingerprint examiners is that many did not meet the minimum recommended requirements for admission into fingerprint training. Some crime laboratories have their own "requirements" but provide no evidence that these are met.

A number of fingerprint examiners, perhaps still a majority, entered the profession before even "recommended" selection standards were put in place. If these standards are important, the profession should insure that examiners who did not meet these standards are provided the additional training, experience and supervision to bring them up to the standards in place. There is no evidence that this remediation is done.

B. Training

With the exception of examiners who have gone through the FBI's training program or been trained in the few other crime laboratories with formal training programs, the majority of fingerprint examiners have not been trained under a uniform training protocol, but receive and continue to receive most of their training informally on-the-job. For those examiners, the level of training, the method(s) taught, the closeness of supervision, and testing to demonstrate acquisition of knowledge and skill are haphazard and unregulated.

In the absence of qualification requirements specified by the profession, examiners who testify in court range widely in their training, and therefore in their expertise.

C. Experience

Improvement with experience is vacuous if measured by elapsed time alone. The profession has not offered documentation that examiners do improve with experience, such as correlations between years of work and supervisor ratings, scores on proficiency tests, or scores on certification tests.

D. Proficiency

Proficiency testing of fingerprint examiner comparison skills suffers from the same deficiencies as selection and training: the profession has not defined a standard, assessed by a validated proficiency testing program, that an examiner must meet in his normal casework in order to be considered proficient.

E. Certification

Unlike proficiency, the IAI does provide a professional standard for certification. However, as described in Chapter 7, the IAI certification test is highly flawed, and cannot be used to document a standard of competency.

F. Court Testimony

No professional organization has defined standards, or how those standards are measured, that describe the qualifications a fingerprint examiner must meet to testify in court.

12.2 Challenges Based on Inadequate Quality Control Standards in Crime Laboratories

Quality controls governing the *operations* of the work in crime laboratories (Chapter 10) and *regulations to prevent examiner exposure to biasing information* (Chapter 9) are not standardized, and for many crime laboratories are nonexistent.

We have never seen a crime laboratory manual that contained a detailed *SOP for fingerprint examinations*. The examiners' comparison processes are unregulated by the laboratories employing examiners.

Explicit *SOPs for verification* are not published in crime laboratory protocols. In practice, crime laboratories rarely follow the substance of the IAI and ASCLD recommendations regarding independent, blind verification, although blind judgments are routinely required in government testing (e.g., drug testing), and in scientific research, because the intrusion of bias and error when judgments are non-blind is well documented and well understood.

SOPs governing supervision of the work of individual examiners are rarely in place. This means that the accuracy of laboratories' work product is not uniformly evaluated and errors arise in chain of custody; and the quality of the work product is lowered.

SOPs regulating error detection, analysis, and modification to prevent further similar errors are rarely in place. In their absence, the laboratory cannot use detected errors to improve performance.

Most crime laboratories do not include *SOPS to control information flow* in their quality control regulations. Without such quality control guidelines in place and enforced, the probability that examiners will be exposed to biasing information is greatly increased, thereby increasing for the laboratory output as a whole the probability of erroneous identifications. Most crime laboratories are part of the police or sheriff's department, allowing biasing discussion and rumors about every case to be part of the everyday interaction in the work setting.

We have never seen a manual that includes *procedures to prevent bias when AFIS* searches are involved (Chapter 9), including the multiple biases introduced by the examiner preprocessing the latent, and viewing exemplars before completely describing the latent.

12.3 Challenges Based on the Absence of Empirical Scientific Evidence

Empirical evidence concerning the validity and reliability of almost every component of fingerprint comparison is missing. The most important of those are highlighted here, including AFIS, effects of bias, uniqueness assumptions about latent prints, the ACE method, and the standards for ACE conclusions.

A. The Reliability and Validity of AFIS-Based Comparisons

In Chapter 6 we described a number of missing measures of the *reliability* and *validity* of the AFIS procedures. There have been no independent tests of the accuracy of different search algorithms. No studies have demonstrated whether different ways of preprocessing of latents for submission produce more accurate results or whether technicians can preprocess one way more consistently than another. The effects of database size and the number of candidates requested have not been studied.

With respect to validity, the profession has assumed that the accuracy of conclusions reached with an AFIS-produced suspect is the same as for an investigation-produced suspect. However, Chapters 6 and 9 describe a number of reasons why this assumption must be tested. This question has never been subjected to experiment.

B. The Strength of Bias Effects During ACE

If the examiner does not record a full description of the physical evidence in the latent before he sees the exemplar, he will tend to use the exemplar to describe the latent (Chapter 9).

No regulatory body in this country requires examiners to complete analysis of the latent first. Many examiners testify that they begin analysis with the latent and exemplar side by side. This procedure is biased. Every time an examiner first identifies a feature in the exemplar and then searches for it in the latent, he increases the probability of an erroneous identification (Chapter 9).

The extent of this biasing practice is untested. In the absence of bench notes, their prevalence is unknowable and untestable.

C. Evidence of Uniqueness

No research has been performed to determine how much pattern, how sharp the detail, and/or how many features or events along ridges in sequence must be present in a latent fingerprint for the probability of an erroneous identification to approach zero. For this reason, the IAI abandoned point counting in 1973.

Conversely, nothing is known about the probability that a latent of poor quality can be identified to more than one exemplar. The absence of these answers undermines the use of latent fingerprint evidence in court to identify one and only one donor as the person who left the latent print.

D. Validity Evidence for the ACE Method

1. The validity of ACE is unknown

The ACE method has never been tested empirically. Latent print examiners are using a method of untested accuracy to make judgments in court (Chapter 8). This is equivalent to a woman who asks what the chances are she's really pregnant, and when the test result says she is, she is told: "The accuracy of the test is unknown."

Examiners are not required to keep bench notes when they perform a comparison, so there is no contemporaneous evidence as to which elements of the prints they compared, which differences they explained, and which features they found in agreement. There is no evidence that they were following the ACE method, or applying it correctly. The work they performed cannot be replicated.

Table 12.1
Prerequisites to Test the Validity of the ACE-V Method

1. Profession writes and adopts a detailed ACE-V manual
2. Profession writes and adopts a detailed report form for ACE-V comparisons
3. Profession adopts an approved training program
4. Profession adopts a validated and reliable proficiency measurement
5. Profession adopts rigorous procedures to prevent bias

2. ACE cannot be tested for its validity

No single version of the ACE method has been accepted as official by the profession, and published versions differ. Exactly which procedures, then, comprise the ACE method so that it can be tested? Table 12.1 summarizes the research results needed *before* ACE can be tested for its validity

3. ACE has no validated standards underlying conclusions

Table 12.2 summarizes what is needed to validate the value, exclusion and identification standards.

The profession has not developed quantitative measures of the data on which conclusions are reached. In the absence of these quantitative measures, the profession cannot apply threshold standards.

With respect to objective value, there is no quantitative, objective metric of the amount of information present in a latent fingerprint. Consequently, there is no threshold amount of information governing the decision value/no value. The method does not specify this threshold standard, so the accuracy of the method in reaching a value judgment cannot be assessed.

With respect to exclusion, the factors that create distortion have never been either fully specified or subjected to testing. There is no research that establishes a measure or metric of the amount of distortion present in a latent print, even though this is one of the most central descriptors required to differentiate correctly between one and two donors. This means that the presence of one or more two-donor pattern dissimilarities, on which exclusion is based, has no empirical foundation. The method does not specify the difference between a distortion and a two-donor pattern dissimilarity, so the accuracy of the method in reaching an exclusion judgment cannot be assessed.

Table 12.2
Requirements for Validated Standards for ACE Conclusions

Analysis: Value Standard
- Quantitative metric of latent print difficulty
- Evidence that examiners use metric consistently
- Profession defines features to describe patterns
- Evidence that examiners use features consistently
- Quantitative metric of feature location-in-space
- Evidence that examiners use metric consistently
- Quantitative metric of type and amount of distortions
- Evidence that examiners recognize type and use metric consistently
- Profession adopts a standard of value based on difficulty

Comparison: One Unexplained Discrepancy Standard
- Profession writes and adopts a bench note form
- Profession defines how to specify relative locations among features in two fingerprints
- Quantitative description of distortion versus difference
- Evidence examiners apply distinction consistently

Evaluation: Numeric Sufficiency Standard
- Profession defines what constitutes agreement
- Evidence examiners evaluate agreement consistently
- Profession adopts a standard for amount of agreement needed for identification based on amount of agreement

Evaluation: Training and Experience Sufficiency Standard
- Profession defines training in quantitative terms
- Profession defines experience in quantitative terms

With respect to identification, the experiment to demonstrate the amount of agreement between two prints to assure a match with a known degree of probability has never been performed. The profession has not agreed upon a quantitative metric of how to count agreement, nor has it specified the amount of agreement needed for an identification. The method does not specify how to quantify agreement, so the accuracy of the method in reaching an identification judgment cannot be assessed.

There is no research that shows examiner accuracy in locating features-in-location, whether they do so by eyeballing, ridge counts, or events-in-sequence on adjacent ridge paths. The profession has not agreed upon a quantitative method to locate features-in-location, nor has it specified the amount of spatial disagreement between two prints needed to exclude or still permissible to identify. The method is unquantified with respect to how to locate a feature and how to locate the same feature across two prints, so the accuracy of the method in assigning agreement/disagreement between features cannot be assessed.

An examiner who testifies in court to an identification justifies his conclusion on the basis of knowledge accumulated during his own training and experience. However, neither amount nor kind of training is quantified, nor is amount or kind of experience. In the absence of validated metrics of training and of experience, no evidence about accuracy can be derived from an individual examiner's training and experience, and no experiment could be performed to assess the validity of this claim.

E. Reliability Evidence for the ACE Method

We consider the lack of reliability for feature descriptions, spatial position, and number of agreements.

1. Feature descriptions

Examiners use Level 1 classifications to exclude suspects, and/or to orient latents (Chapter 3). At present, there is no evidence that these classifications of latent prints are made reliably.

With respect to Level 2 descriptions, research findings indicate that skilled examiners analyzing the same latent print disagree whether Galton features are present (Chapter 8). The ACE method of fingerprint comparison cannot be reliable and valid if experts disagree about the presence of the very features they use to compare and individuate.

Research on the stability of Level 3 details has not been reported, nor is there research evidence to show the amount of examiner agreement on the presence and type of Level 3 features (Chapter 3).

2. Spatial position

Experimental evidence is needed to demonstrate the accuracy and the reliability of the specification of the spatial position of individual features located in a latent fingerprint. This should include a test of differences among the methods currently in use (Chapter 3).

3. Number of features in agreement

Chapter 8 showed that examiners disagreed over the number of agreements they found.

4. Snooker balls

Penrose (1994) points out that Newtonian physics precisely describe the velocity and path of a snooker ball hit with a known degree of force and direction, on a level table with a known amount of friction from its surface. It is a completely deterministic closed system. He also describes the inscrutable uncertainty of the degree of force and direction of a snooker ball after it has been hit several times. The multiple errors in each measurement combine, as do the even less measurable factors such as wind forces in the adjacent county and a sudden sneeze from across the pool table.

Quantification of distortion in a latent print may resemble quantification of the multivariate factors governing the path and force of a repeatedly struck snooker ball. The factors listed in Table 5.4 may prove impossible to measure reliably when combined, so that the distinction between distortion and two-donor pattern dissimilarity may elude quantification. This is an empirical question. If this were true, ACE can never be reliable.

F. How Accurate are Fingerprint Comparisons?

This is an empirical question. It can be answered only by scientific experiment, not by logic, rhetorical arguments, reference to casework in which ground truth is unknown, or wishful thinking. Accuracy is assessed by determining the amount of agreement with ground truth in the conclusions reached by examiners. Errors in conclusions enter from three sources: a seriously distorted latent; the method used for comparison; and the examiner.

1. Latent print contribution to error

As discussed in Chapter 2, latent prints are rarely complete, clear images of fingers, but impoverished, unclear and distorted. As a result, as the quantity and quality of information in the latent decreases, the probability of an erroneous conclusion increases. The quantity and quality (difficulty) of latents has not been quantified, so the extent to which the latent contributes to error in a specific case is presently unknown.

2. ACE method contribution to error

The error rate of the ACE method is unknown, as we discussed in Chapters 5 and 8. We described an experiment that can provide an assessment of the error rate of the method, independent of the difficulty of latents and proficiency of examiners, but this experiment has never been run.

3. Examiner contribution to error

The proficiency of individual examiners (and of the fingerprint profession as a whole) is not assessed by the proficiency and certification tests in present use (see Chapter). The contribution of examiner error to overall error rates currently cannot be evaluated.

12.4 Court Challenges to Fingerprint Evidence

By mid-2009, about 40 American courts have considered some aspect of the admissibility of fingerprint evidence, and most have concluded this evidence is admissible (http://onin.com/fp/daubert_links.html). However, six American court decisions have made negative rulings about the introduction of fingerprint evidence. We review these briefly.

A. *U.S. v. Parks* (1991: Federal District Court, Central District, California, CR 91-398-JSL)

Judge Letts did not allow the fingerprint evidence to be introduced into the trial, because the government's fingerprint examiners disagreed on the standards for sufficiency of agreement for an identification. The Judge concluded that without a reliable sufficiency standard, the testimony of fingerprint examiners was not admissible. Cole (2001) gives a detailed discussion of this decision.

B. *Jacobs v. Virgin Islands* (2002, 53F Appx 651,652 (3rd Cir))

The Virgin Islands trial court ruled (*Virgin Islands v. Jacobs*, 1999) that the government is required to produce evidence of the validity of the methods used to reach the conclusions introduced in court. The Government appealed, but the Third Circuit upheld the trial court's exclusion of the fingerprint evidence.

C. *U.S. v. Plaza I* (2001)

Judge Pollak, in a Daubert hearing on fingerprint methods, ruled that fingerprint evidence did not qualify under Daubert, and restricted examiners to testimony about fingerprint comparisons only. They could not conclude that the defendant and the person who made the crime scene latent print were the same person. After a further Daubert hearing, and a reconsideration (*U.S. v. Plaza* II), Judge Pollak reversed his decision and did not restrict what fingerprint examiners could conclude. See Cole (2005) for a detailed discussion.

D. *Commonwealth of Massachusetts v. Patterson* (2005)

The trial court convicted the defendant based on evidence of an identification to an exemplar from a simultaneous fingerprint. The defendant appealed to the Massachusetts Supreme Judicial Counsel, who ruled that the use of simultaneous fingerprints did not meet Daubert requirements, and remanded the case back to the trial court. Siegel et al. (2005) review the scientific arguments in the case.

E. *New Hampshire v. Langill* (2007, Superior Court of Rockingham County, N.H.)

Judge Coffey excluded the fingerprint evidence from her trial court on the grounds that the identification was improperly verified, and that the examiner failed to keep benchnotes of his procedures. The accuracy of the conclusion accordingly could not be established. The Supreme Court of New Hampshire in *New Hampshire v. Langill* (2008) reversed her ruling on technical grounds, and returned the case to the trial court for retrial.

F. *Maryland v. Rose* (2007: Circuit Court of Baltimore County, Maryland)

In a Frye hearing, Judge Souder (2007) published a ruling that the fingerprint evidence could not be introduced, because the ACE method did not meet the Frye and other scientific criteria. When asked to reconsider her ruling, she reaffirmed it strongly (Souder, 2008).

References

Aitken, C.G.G. (1995). *Statistics and the evaluation of evidence for forensic sciences.* Chichester, England: Wiley.

Altschuler, A. (2003) Quoted on Public Television, "The Plea," produced by Ofra Bickel.

Anthonioz, A., Egli, N., Champod, C., Neumann, C., Puch-Solis, R., and Bromage-Griffiths, A. (2008). "Level Three details and their role in fingerprint identification." *J. Forensic Identification, 58,* 562-589.

Arvizu, J. (2002). Testimony on Mr. Plaza's motion to exclude the government's latent fingerprint evidence, hearing before Judge Pollak, *U.S. v. Plaza,* February 24, 2002.

ASCLD. (2004). 180-Day Study Report: Status and Needs United States Laboratories. Available at www.ncjrs.gov/pdffiles1/nij/grants/213422.pdf.

ASCLD (2006). Strategies for Training. Report of ASCLD. www.ascld.org.

ASCLD (1998). Requirements for Proficiency Testing. Report of ASCLD. www.ascld.org.

Ashbaugh, D.R. (1999) *Quantitative-Qualitative Friction Ridge Analysis: An introduction to basic and advanced ridgeology.* Boca Raton, FL: CRC Press.

Ashbaugh, D.R. (2005a). Proposal for ridges-in-sequence.

Ashbaugh, D.R. (2005b). Friction Ridge Identification Process Worksheet. http://ridgesandfurrows.homestead.com/A_C_E_-V__worksheet.pdf

Ashbaugh, D.R. (2005c). Course notes for Advance Latent Print Comparisons. Taught in Los Angeles, 2005).

Babler, W.J. (1991). "Embryologic development of epidermal ridges and their configuration." *Birth Defects, Originals Article Series, 27*, 95-112.

Bayle, A. (2002). Testimony on Mr. Plaza's motion to exclude the government's latent fingerprint evidence, hearing before Judge Pollak, *U.S. v. Plaza*, February 24, 2002

Beeton, M. (2002). "Friction ridge identification process—Purposed scientific methodology." *The Detail*, 2-18-2002; http://clpex.com.

Black, J. F. (2006). "Pilot Study: The application of ACE-V to simultaneous (cluster) impressions." *J. Forensic Identification*, 56, 933-

Budowle, B., Buscaglia, J., and Perlman, R.S.(2006). "Review of the scientific basis for fingerprint comparisons as a means of identification. Committee Findings and recommendations." *Forensic Science Communication, 8,* 1-16.

Champod, C., Lennard, C. Margot, P. and Stoilovic, M. (2004.) *Fingerprints and other friction ridge skill impressions*. Boca Ratan, Fl.: CRC Press.

Champod, C., and Evett, I.W. (2001). "A probabilistic approach to fingerprint evidence." *J. Forensic Identification, 51*, 101-122.

Cole, S. A. (2001). *Suspect Identities: A history of fingerprinting and criminal identification*. Cambridge, MA.: Harvard University Press.

Cole, S.A. (2004). "Grandfathering evidence: Fingerprint admissibility rulings from Jennings to Llera Plaza and back again." *American Criminal Law Review, 41*, 1189-1276.

Cole, S.A. (2005). "More than zero: Accounting for error in latent fingerprint identifications." *J. Criminal Law and Criminology, 95*, 985-1078.

Cole, S.A. (2007). "Comment on Haber and Haber (2007*)." Law, Probability and Risk, 7.*

Cole, S. (2009) Forensics without uniqueness, conclusions without individualization: the new epistemology of forensic identification. *Law, Probability and Risk, 8,* doi:10.1093/lpr/mgp016.

Cole, S.A., Welling, M., Dioso-Villa, R., and Carpenter, R. (2008). "Beyond the individuality of Fingerprints: a measure of simulated computer latent print source attribution accuracy. " *Law, Probability and Law, 7,* 165-189.

Collaborative Testing Services (various years). (www.collaborativetesting.com).

Commonwealth of Massachusetts v. Patterson, 840, NE 2d 12.24 (Mass, 2005).

Cowger, J.F. (1993). *Friction ridge skin: comparison and identification of finger-prints*. Boca Raton, FL: CRC Press

Dabbs, G.R. (2009). Is Dwight right? Can the maximum height of the scapula be used for accurate estimation of sex. *J. Forensic Science, 54,* 529-530.

Dror, I.E., Peron, A., Hind, S., and Charlton, D. (2005). "When emotions get the better of us: The effects of cognitive top-down processing in matching fingerprints." *Applied Cognitive Psychology, 19,* 799-808.

Dror, I.E., Charlton, D., and Peron, A. (2006). "Contextual information renders experts vulnerable to making erroneous identifications." *J. Forensic Identification, 56,* 74-78.

Dror, I.E., and Fraser-MacKensie, P.A.F. (2008). "Cognitive biases in human perception, judgment and decision making: bridging theory and the real world." In K. Rossmo (Ed.), *Criminal Investigation Failures* (Ch 5, pp 53-67). London: Taylor and Francis.

Dror, I.E., and Charlton, D. (2006). "Why experts make mistakes." *J. Forensic Identification, 56,* 600-616.

Evett, Z.W., and Williams, R.L. (1996). "Review of the 16 point fingerprint standard in England and Wales." *J. Forensic Identification, 46,* 49-73.

Federal Bureau of Identification (1988, last edition). *The Science of Fingerprints: Classification and uses.* United States Department of Justice

Federal Bureau of Identification (1998). Mitchell survey. Introduced at *U.S. v. Mitchell*, 365F (3d. Circuit). 1998.

Federal Bureau of Identification (2007) A research program announced at the 2007 IAI Education Conference, San Diego, CA.

Fisher, B.A.J. (2003). *Techniques of Crime Scene Investigation* (7th Edition). Boca Ratan, Fl: CRC Press.

Fitzpatrick, F. (2008). "Whither Accreditation." *Identification News, 38,* 9-10

Galton, F. (1896). *Finger Prints.* London: McMillin.

Garrett, R.J. (2009). "Editorial comments." *IDentification News, 39,* April/May, p 1; 14-15.

Grieve, D.L. (2001). "Simon Says." *J. Forensic Identification, 51,* 85-96.

Gutowski, S. (2006). "Error rates in fingerprint examinations: the view from 2006." *The Forensic Bulletin,* Summer, 18-19.

Haber, R.N. (2002). Testimony on Mr. Plaza's motion to exclude the government's latent fingerprint evidence, hearing before Judge Pollak, *U.S. v. Plaza,* February 24, 2002

Haber, R.N. (2003). "Fingerprint science." Columbia Broadcasting System 60 Minutes, January 5, 2003.

Haber, R.N., and Haber, L. (2000). "Experiencing, remembering and reporting events; The cognitive psychology of eyewitness testimony." *Psychology, Public Policy and Law, 6,* 1057-1097.

Haber, L., and Haber, R.N. (2004). "Error rates for human latent fingerprint examiners." In N. Ratha and R. Bolle (Eds.), *Automatic Fingerprint Recognition,* pps 339-360. New York: Springer Verlag.

Haber, L. and Haber, R.N. (2007). "Scientific validation of fingerprint evidence under Daubert." *Law, Probability and Risk, 17,* 87-102.

Haber, L. and Haber. R.N. (2006). "Letter to the Editor regarding: A report of latent print examiner accuracy during training exercises." J. Forensic Identification, 56; *J. Forensic Identification, 56-*93-499.

Haber, R.N., and Hershenson, M. (1980). *The psychology of visual perception.* (second edition), New York: Holt, Rinehart & Winston.

Haber, R.N., and Levin, C. (2001). "The independence of size perception and distance perception." *Perception and Psychophysics, 63,* 1140-1152.

Hall, L.J., and Player, E. (2008). "Will the introduction of an emotional context affect fingerprint analyses and decision making." *Forensic Science International, 181,* 36-39.

Holman, R. (2005). Next generation IAFIS program overview. Presentation to the 2005 IAI Education Conference, Dallas, 2005.

Huber, R.A., (1959). "Expert witness." *Criminal Law Quarterly, 2*, 276-297.

International Association for Identification Latent Print Certification Board (2009). *IDentification News, 39*, April/May, p. 21.

International Association for Identification (2009) *Directory*.

International Association for Identification (1973) "Standards committee report." *Law Enforcement Bulletin*, pp 7-8.

Interpol European Expert Group on Fingerprint Identification (IEEGGI II) (2005). "Method for fingerprint identification." www.interpol.int.

Jacobs v. Virgin Islands (2002).53F Appx 651,652 (3rd Circuit), 2002.

Kaye, D.H. (2003). "From snowflakes to fingerprints: A dubious courtroom prof and the uniqueness of fingerprints." *International Statistical Review*, 521.

Komarinski, P. (2005). *Automated fingerprint identification systems (AFIS)*. London, England: Elsevier Academic Press.

Koppl, R. (2005). "How to improve forensic science." *European J. Law and Economics. 20*, 255-286.

Langenburg, G. (2004). "Pilot study: a statistical analysis of the ACE-V method- analysis stage." *J. Forensic Identification*, 54, 64-74.

Langenburg, G. (2008). "A performance study of the ACE-V process: A pilot study to measure the accuracy, precision, reproducibility, repeatability and bias ability of conclusions resulting from the ACE-V process." *J. Forensic Identification, 59*, 219-257.

Langenburg, G., Champod, C., and Wertheim, P. (2009)" Testing for potential contextual bias effects during the verification stage of ACE-V methodology when conducting fingerprint comparisons." *J. Forensic Science, 50*, 1-12.

Lee, H.C., and Gaensslen, R.E. (2001). "Methods of latent fingerprint development." In H.C. Lee and R.E. Gaensslen (Eds.), *Advances in Fingerprint Technology* (Second Edition), pp. 105-175. Baco Ratan, Fl.: CRC Press.

Legal Challenges to Fingerprints (2008) http://onin.com/fp/daubert_links.html.

Leo, W. (1998). "Distortion versus dissimilarity in friction ridge skin." J. *Forensic Identification, 48,* 125-129.

Maryland v. Bryan Rose (2007) Case # K-06-0545, Baltimore County Circuit Court, Oct, 19, 2007.

McCabe, R. M. (2004). "Interoperability standards." In N. Rathe and R. Bolle (Eds.), *Automatic Fingerprint Recognition systems,* pp. 433-452. New York: Springer Verlag.

Meagher, S. (1999). Testimony in USA v. Mitchell before Judge Joiner, US District Court, District of Eastern Pennsylvania.

Meagher, S. B., Budowle, B., and Ziesig, D. (1998). "50K v. 50K fingerprint comparison test." In Daubert hearing before Justice Joiner, July 8-9, 1999 U.S. Bryon Mitchell, U.S. District Court PA (3d).

Meagher, S. (2002). Testimony on Mr. Plaza's motion to exclude the government's latent fingerprint evidence, hearing before Judge Pollak, *U.S. v. Plaza*, February 24, 2002.

Meagher, S. (2003). Columbia Broadcasting System 60 Minutes, January 5, 2003.

Meagher, S. (2007) Testimony in *Maryland v. Rose*, Case No. K-o6-0545, Baltimore County Circuit Court, May 30, 2007,

Menzel, E.R., (2001). "Fingerprint detection with photoluminescent nanoparticles." In H.C. Lee and Gaensslen (Eds.), *Advances in Fingerprint technology.*

Mnookin, J.L. (2007). "The validity of latent fingerprint identifications: confession of a fingerprinting moderate." *Law, Probability and Risk, 7,* 127.

National Academy of Sciences. (2009). *Strengthening Forensic Sciences in the United States: a Path Forward.* Washington DC: National Academies Press.

New Hampshire v. Langill (2007) (No. 050S-1129). Superior Court of Rockingham County, N.H.

New Hampshire v. Langill (2008) State of New Hampshire Supreme Court. April 4, 2008. Review of New Hampshire v. Langill (No. 050S-1129). Superior Court of Rockingham County, N.H.

Office of the Inspector General. (2006). *Review of the FBI's handling of the Brandon Mayfield case.* Washington, D.C., US Department of Justice (Steven Fine, Inspector General).

Olsen, R.D., Sr., and Lee, H.C. (2001). "Identification of latent prints." In H.C. Lee and Gaensslen, (Eds.). *Advances in Fingerprint technology* (2nd edition), pp. 41-61. Baco Ratan, FL: CRC Press.

Penrose, R. (1994). *Shadows of the Mind.* New York: Oxford University Press.

Peterson, J.L., and Markham, P.N. (1995). "Crime laboratory proficiency testing results 1978-1991: II: resolving questions of common origin." *J. Forensic Identification, 40,* 1009.

Peterson, M.A., and Rhodes, C. (2003). "Analytic and holistic processing- the view through different lenses." In M.A. Peterson and C. Rhodes (Eds.), *Perception of Faces, Objects and Scenes,* pp. 3-20, New York: Oxford University Press.

Prabhaker, S., and Jain, A. K. (2004). Fingerprint matching. In N. Ratha & R. Bolle (Eds.) (2004*). Automatic Fingerprint Recognition Systems* (pp. 229-248). New York: Springer-Verlag.

Ratha, N., and Bolle, R. (Eds.) (2004*). Automatic Fingerprint Recognition Systems.* New York: Springer-Verlag.

Risinger, D.M., Saks, M.J., Thompson, W.C., and Rosenthal, R. (2002). "The Daubert/Kumho implications of observer effects in Forensic Science: Problems of expectation and suggestion." *California Law Review, 90,*1-56.

Scheck, B., Neufeld, P., and Dwyer, J. (2001). Actual Innocence: When Justice Goes Wrong and How to Make it Right. New York: Signet Books

Siegel, D.M. et al. (2006). "The reliability of latent fingerprint individualization: Brief of Amici Curiae of Scientists, Scholars and the New England Innocence Project (*Commonwealth v. Patterson*)." *Criminal Law Review, 42,* 21-.

Smith, K. (2002). Testimony on Mr. Plaza's motion to exclude the government's latent fingerprint evidence, hearing before Judge Pollak, *U.S. v. Plaza*, February 24, 2002.

Smith, R. (2004). Latent print unit evaluation. Report to Capt. Thomas Dowd, Supervision of Identification Bureau, Boston Police Dept, Sept 5, 2004.

Smrz, M.A., Burmestein, S.G.,, Einseln, A., Fisher, C.L., Fran, R., Stacey, R.B., Thesin, C.E., and Budowle, B. (2006). "Review of FBI latent print unit processes and recommendations to improve practices and quality." *J. Forensic Identification, 56,* 402-434.

Souder, S. (2007). Memorandum Decision. *Maryland v. Bryan Rose.* October 2007

Souder, S. (2008). Reconsideration of Memorandum Decision. *Maryland v. Bryan Rose*, February 2008.

Stacey, R.B. (2004). "Report on the erroneous fingerprint individualization in the Madrid training bombing case." *J. Forensic Identification, 54,* 706-718.

Stoney, D.A. (2001). "Measurement of fingerprint individuality." In H.C. Lee and Gaensslen (eds.), *Advances in Fingerprint technology* (2nd ed.), pp. 327-387. Baco Ratan, FL: CRC Press.

SWGFAST (2002a). Fingerprint examination methodology for latent fingerprint examination. www.swgfast.org/Friction_Ridge_Examination_Methodology_for_Latent_Print_Examiners_1.01.pdf

SWGFAST (2002b) training to competence for latent fingerprint examiners, ver 2.1, 8-22-02. www.swgfast.org.

SWGFAST (2004). "Guidelines for latent print proficiency testing program." 9/11/03, ver. 1.0. *J. Forensic Identification, 54,* 354-357.

SWGFAST (2004). "Standards for conclusions." 9/11/03, v.1.0. J. *Forensic Identification,* 358-359.

SWGFAST (2006). Quality assurance guidelines for latent print examiners. 9.28.06.ver. 3.0. www.swgfast.org

SWGFAST (2009) Glossary. www.swgfast.org.

Tanaka, J.W., and Farah, M.J. (2003). "The holistic representation of faces." In M.A. Peterson and C. Rhodes (Eds.), *The perception of faces, objects and scenes*, pp. 53-74. New York: Oxford University Press.

Tangen, J.M., and Vokey, J.R. (2009). "Fingerprint identification: on the psychophysics of identification." *Quarterly Journal of Experimental Psychology.*

Tavris, C., and Aronson, E. (2006). *Mistakes were made, but not by me.* Orlando, FL: Harcourt.

Thompson, W.C., Taroni, F., and Aitkin, C.G.G. (2003). "How the probability of a false positive affects the value of DNA statistics." J. *Forensic Science, 46*, 1-8.

Thornton, J.I. (1977). "The one dissimilarity doctrine in fingerprint identification. " *J.Forensic Identification, 56*, 345-356.

Triplett, M., and Cooney, L. (2006). "The etiology of ACE-V and its present use: An exploration of the relationship between ACDE-V and the scientific method of hypothesis testing." *Journal of Forensic Investigation, 56*, 245-253.

U.S. v. Bryan Mitchell (1999) Cr. No. 96-407 (Eastern District of Pennsylvania.

U.S. v. Havvard 117 F.Sup 2d, 848 (S.D. Ind, 2000)

U.S. v. Mitchell, 365 F. 3d 215, 246 (3d Cir 2004)

U.S. v. Parks (1991). Central District of California, CR 91-358-JSL.

U.S. v. Plaza 179F Supp 2d 492 (ED Pa, 2002). Known as Plaza 1.

U.S. v. Plaza, 188F. Supp. 2d E.D. PA, 2002. Known as Plaza 2.

U.S. v. Robert Baines (2009) United States Court of Appeals, Tenth District (No. 08-2098), July 20, 2008. Appeal from the US District Court (District of New Mexico) (No 2:06-CR 09797-MV-3).

Virgin Islands v. Jacobs. 634 F. Supp. 933 (D. Virgin Islands) 186.

Vokey, J.R., Tangen, J. M., and Cole, S.A. (2008). "On the preliminary psychophysics of identification." *Quarterly Journal of Experimental Psychology,*

Wells, G. L., Memon, A., and Penrod, S.D (2007). "Eyewitness evidence: improving its probative value." *Psychological Science in the Public Interest, 7*, No.2, 45-75.

Wertheim, K, Langenburg, G., and Moenssens, A.A. (2006). "A report of latent print examiner accuracy during training exercises." *Journal Forensic Identification, 56*, 55-92.

Wertheim, K., Langenburg, G., and Moenssens, A.A. (2006). "Authors' reply to letter re: A report of latent print examiner accuracy during training exercises." *J. Forensic Identification, 56*, 493-499.

Wertheim, K. (2001) (1 Weekly Detail, Aug. 1, 2001. http://www.clpex.com/Articles/TheDetail/1-99/TheDetail01.htm

Wertheim, K. (2003). Class notes for training course in fingerprint comparative method. Santa Ana, CA, December 1-5, 2003.

Wertheim, K., and Maceo, A. (2003). "The critical stages of friction ridge and pattern function." *J. Forensic Identification, 52*, 34-85.

Wertheim, P. (2000). "Scientific comparison and identification of fingerprints evidence." *The Print, 16*, Sept/Oct, 2000, 1-8.

About the Authors

Lyn Haber, Ph.D.

Lyn Haber has four degrees, including a B.A. from Brandeis University, an M.A. and Ph.D. from the University of California at Berkeley, and an M.A. from the University of Illinois at Chicago. She has taught graduate and undergraduate science courses at Temple University, the University of Rochester, Stanford University and the University of Illinois, rising from the rank of Instructor to Full Professor. She is presently a partner in Human Factors Consultants. She has published 150 scientific articles and books, and presented at 150 scientific conferences. She has been retained in nearly 200 criminal and civil litigation cases, and has testified in both federal and state superior courts.

Ralph Norman Haber, Ph.D.

Ralph Haber has a B.A. from the University of Michigan, a M.A. from Wesleyan University, a Ph.D. from Stanford University, and postgraduate training from the Medical Research Council at Cambridge, England. He has taught graduate and undergraduate courses at San Francisco State College, Yale University, the University of Rochester, Stanford University, and the University of Illinois, rising from the rank of Instructor to Full Professor. He was chairman of the Department of Psychology at the University of Rochester. He is presently a partner in Human Factors Consultants. He has published 250 scientific articles and books, and presented his work at 150 scientific conventions and conferences. He has been retained in nearly 200 criminal and civil litigation cases, and has testified in both federal and state superior courts.

Human Factors Consultants: A Consulting Partnership

Lyn and Ralph Haber are joint partners of Human Factors Consultants, a firm that has provided consultation, research and expert testimony to the legal profession on identification matters since 1980. They are both research scientists specializing in the evaluation of research and practice of forensic identifications, and in the underlying cognitive processes of perception, memory, decision making, judgment, language, comprehension, training and reporting. Their consultation with lawyers has involved cases including finger and eyewitness evidence, assessment of language comprehension, second language learning, and the uses of language in racial, sexual and other social contexts, and human factors issues in car, truck and airplane accidents, industrial accidents, and issues of warnings and risk.

Human Factors Consultants has also provided expertise and research through contracts with the U.S. Government on operator training for automobiles, freight locomotives, trucks, automatic subway systems, military aircraft, commuting traffic, air traffic and rail traffic control and dispatching. They have written and tested training manuals for these tasks. They have carried out research on fitting products to people, including shoes for Nike, Inc., and eyewear for Bausch & Lomb.

Training in Fingerprint Comparisons
Lyn and Ralph Haber have jointly taken three training courses in latent fingerprint comparison since 2003, offered by Richard Walley formerly of the San Diego Police Department, Kasey Wertheim of the University of West Virginia, and David Ashbaugh of the Royal Canadian Mounted Police (Retired). The latter two courses were under the auspices of the IAI training programs. These comprised 104 classroom hours. The courses focused on the method for performing latent print comparisons, the scientific issues underlying fingerprint identifications, and training and proficiency testing of latent fingerprint examiners.

Testimony at Trial on Fingerprint Cases
Between 2001 and mid-2009, the Habers have been retained 26 times to provide consultation, affidavits, and hearing and trial testimony in cases involving fingerprint evidence, eleven in federal courts. They have testified in 11 (5 in Federal court), and submitted affidavits in 5 more. The courts have ruled in every case that they were qualified to provide testimony or documentation on fingerprint science, the validity of methods to compare fingerprints, and the application of those methods in the instant case. They provided the testimony in the Frye hearing in *Maryland v. Rose*, after which the court excluded all fingerprint evidence being offered by the state. The lists of these cases can be found on their website: www.humanfactorsconsultants.com.

Research Publications and Conference Presentations on Fingerprint Science
From 2001 to mid-2009, they have jointly published six articles on fingerprint science. They have given nineteen presentations, of which nine were invited: two to university audiences, two to a conference of public defenders, three to examiners working in police and sheriff crime laboratories, one to a conference of private investigators, and one to the California Commission on the Fair Administration of Justice. The remaining ten presentations included five at scientific conventions, two as part of continuing legal education training, and three to Innocence Project trainees and lawyers. A complete listing of these scientific publications and presentations are found on their website: www.humanfactorsconsultants.com.

Index